TEACHER'S RESOURCE MASTERS

BLACKLINE MASTERS AND TEACHER'S MANUAL

GRADE 5

SPOTLIGHT on MUSIC

SERIES AUTHORS

Judy Bond	Michael Jothen
René Boyer	Chris Judah-Lauder
Margaret Campbelle-Holman	Carol King
Emily Crocker	Vincent P. Lawrence
Marilyn C. Davidson	Ellen McCullough-Brabson
Robert de Frece	Janet McMillion
Virginia Ebinger	Nancy L.T. Miller
Mary Goetze	Ivy Rawlins
Betsy M. Henderson	Susan Snyder
John Jacobson	Gilberto D. Soto

Kodály Contributing Consultant
Sr. Lorna Zemke

Macmillan
McGraw-Hill

INTRODUCTION

This *Teacher's Resource Masters* book contains supplementary activities for *Spotlight on Music.* These Resource Masters include the following:

- A variety of activities that reinforce or review concepts taught in the lessons. Some Resource Masters emphasize manipulative activities, while others offer opportunities for written or aural activities.

- Student and teacher support to complete the Creative Unit Projects. Students can use the Resource Masters to guide them through the project and complete a self-assessment at the project's conclusion. Teachers are also given an assessment rubric for each Creative Unit Project.

- Listening maps that provide visual guidance for students as they listen to specific music selections. The listening maps help students identify melodic and rhythmic patterns, tone color, form, and other musical elements. Suggestions for how to use these listening maps in the classroom are provided at the beginning of the Listening Map section.

- Review questions for each unit. The Spotlight Your Success! Resource Masters allow students to record their responses to the review questions at the completion of each unit. The Read and Listen questions and music examples are recorded.

- Scripts and lyrics for the musical theater Broadway For Kids.

- Sign language versions of selected songs using American Sign Language.

All Resource Masters may be duplicated for classroom use. Each Resource Master is cross referenced to a specific unit and lesson that it was designed to support.

ACKNOWLEDGMENTS

Grateful acknowledgment is given to the following publishers. Every effort has been made to trace the ownership of all copyrighted material and to secure the necessary permissions to reprint these selections. In the case of some selections for which acknowledgment is not given, extensive research has failed to locate the copyright holders.

Meredith Willson's **THE MUSIC MAN JUNIOR**
Book, Music, and Lyrics by Meredith Willson
Story by Meredith Willson and Franklin Lacey
© 1950, 1954, 1957, 1958 by Frank Music Corp. and Rinimer Corporation.
Copyright renewed 1978 by Frank Music Corp. and Rinimer Corporation.
International Copyright Secured. All Rights Reserved.
The Music Man Junior Libretto/Vocal book © 2001 by MTI Enterprises, Inc.
Broadway Junior and **The Broadway Junior Collection** are trademarks of MTI Enterprises, Inc.

TABLE OF CONTENTS

SPOTLIGHT ON CONCEPTS

SPOTLIGHT ON CELEBRATIONS

LISTENING MAPS

SPOTLIGHT ON SIGNING

School-to-Home Letter

Dear Family,

Your fifth grader is in for a new and exciting school year as he or she learns more about music! In our class, students will continue to learn new skills and concepts that will form the foundation for a lifetime of musical enjoyment.

In this first unit, students will learn and play songs and music representing the rich cultural heritage of the United States. They will explore the concepts of rhythm and beat, learning more complex rhythms and how they are written and used. Listening to and singing traditional American music will serve as an introduction to pentatonic scales, pitch, range, and keys, as well as to the special sounds—the tone color—of various bluegrass instruments. Musical texture will be reinforced through the creation of rhythmic pieces. Students will have the chance to get up and dance while learning the musical form, a piece of swing music. Lastly, your student will explore how dynamics are used in marching band and orchestral music and explore theme and variations form. At home you can reinforce your student's learning by sharing some American music that you love.

I am here to help *you* help your student explore our musical world. Producing a music program at school requires much work and many extra hands. Thank you for whatever assistance you can offer this year: at home, at school, or both. Together we can create a musical learning experience for each student that will enrich his or her life for many years to come.

Sincerely,

Fifth Grade Music Teacher

School-to-Home Letter

Estimada Familia,

Su hijo de quinto grado llegó y debe prepararse para un nuevo y emocionante año escolar a medida que aprende más sobre la música. En nuestra clase, los alumnos continuarán aprendiendo nuevas habilidades y conceptos que constituirán los cimientos para un disfrute musical de por vida.

En esta primera unidad, los alumnos aprenderán y tocarán canciones y músicas que representan el rico legado musical de los Estados Unidos. Continuarán explorando los conceptos de ritmo y compás al aprender ritmos más complejos y el modo en que se escriben y utilizan. Escuchar y cantar canciones tradicionales norteamericanas servirá como introducción a las escalas pentatónicas, gamas de tonos y teclas, y también a los sonidos especiales—el color del tono—de varios instrumentos de la música *folk 'Bluegrass'*. Se reforzará la textura musical mediante la creación de piezas rítmicas. Los alumnos tendrán la oportunidad de levantarse y bailar mientras aprenden la forma y esquema musical del *swing*. Por último, su hijo explorará la dinámica musical se utilizan en la música de las orquestas y en la de las bandas escolares. En su hogar, usted puede reforzar el aprendizaje de su hijo compartiendo la música de los Estados Unidos que a usted le guste.

Estoy aquí para ayudar a su hijo a explorar nuestro mundo musical. Hacer un programa de música en la escuela requiere mucho trabajo y muchas manos extra. Le agradecemos cualquier colaboración que nos pueda ofrecer durante este año: desde su hogar, en la escuela o en ambos lugares. Juntos podemos crear una experiencia musical de aprendizaje para su niño/a que enriquecerá su vida en los años venideros.

Atentamente,

Maestra de Música de Quinto Grado

Creative Unit Project   RESOURCE MASTER

Your project for Unit 1 is to write your own music! By following the steps, your group will create a rhythm pattern, a melody, and ostinatos. Then you will put it all together for a performance. Be sure to follow the directions for each step carefully. The rhythms, pitches, and choice of instruments for your music must work well together *and* with another piece of music you will be using in your performance.

STEP 1 *(Complete this step after studying Lesson 1 in the unit.)*
Compose the first three measures of a four-measure rhythm in $\frac{4}{4}$ meter. (The fourth measure is provided for you.) Use these elements: ♩, ♫, ♩. Try different combinations, remembering that you are working with $\frac{4}{4}$ meter. When you are happy with your measures, notate the rhythms on the staff below. Practice the pattern on an unpitched percussion instrument of your choice.

STEP 2 *(Complete this step after studying Lesson 2 in the unit.)*
Compose a melody for the four-measure rhythm pattern you created in Step 1. Use pitches from the C-pentatonic scale: *do re mi so la do'*. The final pitch should be C, *do*. Write the melody on the staff below. Then sing it or play it on a pitched instrument of your choice.

STEP 3 *(Complete this step after studying Lesson 3 in the unit.)*
Now compose two 2-measure ostinatos to accompany your melody. Use low and high *do* in C pentatonic. Choose from these rhythmic elements: ♫, ♩, ♪, 𝅗𝅥, 𝄼, 𝅝, and 𝄻 Notate your ostinatos on the staffs below. Practice them on a pitched instrument.

Creative Unit Project

RESOURCE MASTER 1•3

STEP 4 *(Complete this step after studying Lesson 4 in the unit.)*
You've heard the old saying, "Practice makes perfect." Now is the time to practice, practice, practice. You have the melody and the ostinatos that you wrote. Below, you will find the refrain for "In That Great Git'n Up Mornin'." Now it's time to put them all together.

Begin by singing the refrain for "In That Great Git'n Up Mornin'." This will be the A section of your song. Then play your melody with the ostinatos. (Be sure to use the same tempo you used when singing the A section.) This will be the B section of your song. After you have practiced both sections, try creating different forms: A B A, A A B A, A B B A, and so on. Decide which form you like the best. Practice the music until you are ready to perform.

In That Great Git'n Up Mornin'

Rhythm 4 You

Clap these rhythms. Then circle the beat in line **b** that changes from line **a** each time. Sometimes you will circle more than one beat.

1. a. [rhythm notation]

   b. [rhythm notation]

2. a. [rhythm notation]

   b. [rhythm notation]

3. a. [rhythm notation]

   b. [rhythm notation]

Circle the rhythm in each pair that contains four beats.

4. a. [rhythm notation]

   b. [rhythm notation]

5. a. [rhythm notation]

   b. [rhythm notation]

Fill in the blanks with ♩, ♫, or ᘔ, so that each rhythm has four beats.

6. [rhythm notation]

7. [rhythm notation]

8. [rhythm notation]

9. [rhythm notation]

10. [rhythm notation]

C-Pentatonic Scale

RESOURCE MASTER

Draw a line from the melody pattern on the staff to the matching pitch syllable names.

1. [melody staff]   a. *re mi so do*

2. [melody staff]   b. *mi so re la*

3. [melody staff]   c. *do la la re*

4. [melody staff]   d. *so re mi mi*

5. [melody staff]   e. *la do re so*

Write the correct pitch letter names for each pattern using C D E G A.

6. [melody staff]   9.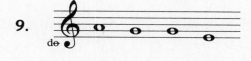

___ ___ ___ ___

7. [melody staff]   10.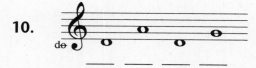

___ ___ ___ ___

8. [melody staff]

___ ___ ___ ___

Caribbean Cruise

RESOURCE MASTER 1•6

The exciting beat of Latin music we hear today includes several kinds of music. With the islands of the Caribbean all fairly close together, you can take a quick cruise to find out more about some of the Latin music from that area.

The **Dominican Republic** is home to *merengue* music. *Merengue* is dance music that is usually played on drums, marimba, and accordion. *Merengue* is also popular in other parts of the Caribbean and throughout South America.

Reggae music began in **Jamaica.** *Reggae* has a very strong accent on the second and fourth beat of each measure. Bob Marley, a well-known musician, helped make *reggae* music popular outside Jamaica.

Bomba music comes from **Puerto Rico.** *Bomba* is a "call-and-response" style of music. In call-and-response music, a leader plays or sings a part and the rest of the musicians reply. Drums are usually used to accompany *bomba* music.

The island nation of **Cuba** is home to *son* music. *Son* is dance music from the rural areas of the island. Two well-known dances, the rumba and the mambo, are based on *son* music and became very popular in the United States in the 1930s and 1940s.

Look at the map showing the islands mentioned above. Write the name of the musical style next to the island where it began.

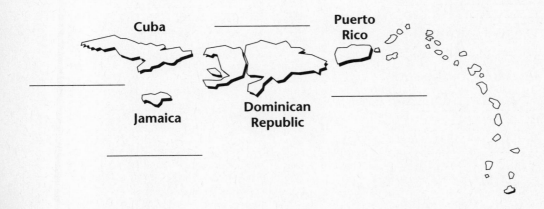

Song Ranges

RESOURCE MASTER

"God Bless America" was written by Irving Berlin who wrote hundreds of songs for Broadway and Hollywood musicals. Many people think that "God Bless America" is one of the best patriotic songs ever written.

Born in Siberia, Russia in 1888, young Irving Berlin came to the United States with his family at the age of five. He grew up in New York City and was still a boy when his father died. He sold newspapers and sang on street corners to help support his family.

Although Berlin had no formal musical training, he taught himself piano and began composing songs. His first published song was "Alexander's Ragtime Band" in 1911. During his long career, Berlin wrote and published over a thousand songs. Many of those songs became popular American classics, such as "White Christmas," "There's No Business Like Show Business," "Easter Parade," and, of course, "God Bless America." Berlin died in 1989 at the age of 101 and his legacy of great popular music lives on.

Look at the notes to "God Bless America" on page 4 of your music book. Starting with the lowest note and ending with the highest note, make a list of all the different pitches you find. Write the notes on the blank staff below.

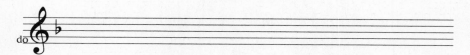

1. What is the lowest note in the song? _____

2. What is the highest note in the song? _____

3. What is the range of the song? _____

Song Ranges

RESOURCE MASTER 1•7

Now look at the notes of the verses of "Sing, America Sing." Make a list of pitches, starting with the lowest note and ending with the highest note of the melody, of all the different notes you find. Write the notes on the blank staff below.

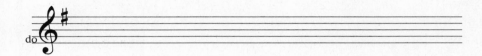

4. What is the lowest note in the melody? _____

5. What is the highest note in the melody? _____

6. What is the range of the melody? _____

Sing, America Sing!

Words and Music by
Emily Crocker and John Jacobson

Name _____ Date _____

Mid-Unit Review

Complete the crossword puzzle.
Each clue is about a vocabulary
word you have learned.

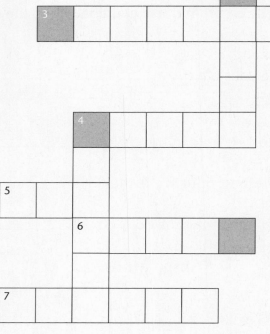

Down

1 Interval made up of a pitch and the next pitch that uses the same pitch name

2 The silent pulse in music

4 Combination of long and short sounds and silences

Across

3 Song with a religious message on the surface

4 Distance from the lowest to the highest pitch of a song

5 Relationship of a series of pitches to the tonal center

6 The speed of the beat

7 The style of popular music and dance from Columbia

BONUS WORD!

Write the letters from the shaded squares of the puzzle: ___ ___ ___ ___ ___

Unscramble the letters. What is the vocabulary word? _____

What does the word mean? _____

Name _____ Date _____

Bluegrass Band

The members of Nickel Creek were around your age when they first formed their band. Suppose that you are going to form a five-member bluegrass band. Think about the timbre of each instrument generally used in bluegrass music. Match it to the personality of a friend or family member. (Don't forget yourself!) Explain why each person "goes with" the instrument you have chosen. Then name your band.

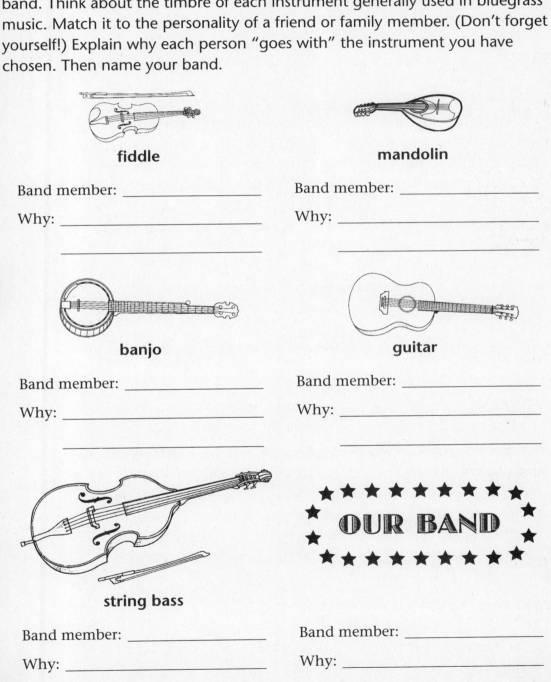

fiddle

Band member: _____

Why: _____

_____

mandolin

Band member: _____

Why: _____

_____

banjo

Band member: _____

Why: _____

_____

guitar

Band member: _____

Why: _____

_____

string bass

Band member: _____

Why: _____

_____

★ OUR BAND ★

Band member: _____

Why: _____

_____

Name _____ Date _____

Adding Layers

RESOURCE MASTER **1•10**

You and your group are going to create a song. One person will start the rhythmic piece by creating and repeating a rhythmic phrase. The next person will add a layer to the texture by clapping that rhythm. Then the third person will add a layer by stomping his or her feet to the same rhythm, and so on.

Form groups of three to five people, and assign each person a number starting with 1.

Number 1 will begin the rhythmic piece. You need to think of a simple rhythmic phrase to speak, such as "Reach up high" or "Chickens and catfish." If you are having trouble coming up with a phrase on your own, have the group help out. Your phrase is going to be the first layer of the song.

Start repeating your phrase. Make sure that you keep the same tempo each time you speak.

Now, **Number 2** comes in. **Start clapping** the rhythm of Number 1's words.

Number 3, it's your turn. **Start stomping** your feet to the rhythm of Number 1's words.

Number 4, add a noise in the rhythm using your mouth.

And finally, **Number 5, add a different noise or repeat a different word or words** to the rhythm.

Keep this up until your teacher gives you the signal to finish. As an extra challenge, see whether you can bring your rhythmic piece back down to one person. Another challenge would be to each use a different rhythm at the same time, keeping the same tempo.

12

USE WITH GRADE 5, UNIT 1, LESSON 6

Name _____ Date _____

Musical Form

Identify the sections in the song below by writing the letter A or B next to the appropriate staff. After you have finished, write the form of the piece on the lines provided below the song title.

**Little David,
Play on Your Harp**

African
American Spiritual

Lit-tle Da-vid, play on your harp, Hal - le - lu! Hal - le - lu!

(Fine)

Lit - tle Da-vid, play on your harp, Hal - le - lu!_____

1. Lit - tle Da - vid was a shep - herd boy, He
2. Old____ Da - vid was a might - y king, and

*Go back to the beginning
and sing to the end.
(Da Capo al Fine)*

slew Go - li - ath and shout - ed for joy._____
all the peo - ple came____ to sing._____

_____

_____

_____

Name That Symbol!

RESOURCE MASTER

Match each symbol to its name or the words that describe it.
Write the correct letter in the blank.

_____ 1.	f	**a.**	quarter rest
_____ 2.	𝄞	**b.**	very soft
_____ 3.	mf	**c.**	meter signature
_____ 4.	𝅗𝅥	**d.**	crescendo
_____ 5.	<	**e.**	forte
_____ 6.	▬	**f.**	very loud
_____ 7.	pp	**g.**	treble clef
_____ 8.	♪	**h.**	medium loud
_____ 9.	▬	**i.**	eighth note
_____ 10.	$\frac{4}{4}$	**j.**	get softer
_____ 11.	𝄽	**k.**	medium soft
_____ 12.	♩	**l.**	half rest
_____ 13.	mp	**m.**	half note
_____ 14.	ff	**n.**	quarter note
_____ 15.	>	**o.**	whole rest

Spotlight Your Success! RESOURCE MASTER

Review. Circle the correct answer.

1. Which list of note values goes in order from shortest to longest?

   a. eighth note, half note, sixteenth note, whole note

   b. whole note, quarter note, half rest, eighth note

   c. half note, whole note, quarter note, eighth note

   d. eighth note, quarter note, half note, whole note

2. Which pitches are in a pentatonic scale?

   a. *do re mi fa so*   b. *do re mi so ti*   c. *do re mi so la*

3. What are the names of these pitches?

   a. C' E G D A C   b. C D E G A C'   c. D' E' G A B D

4. Which symbols show these rests: half rest, quarter rest, whole rest, eighth rest?

   a. ♪ 𝄽 ▬ ▬   b. ▬ 𝄽 ▬ ♪   c. ▬ ▬ 𝄽 ♪

Read and Listen. Circle the correct answer.

1. **Read** these rhythms. Then listen. Which rhythm do you hear?

   a. ♩ ♫ ♩ 𝄾   b. ♫ ♫ ♩ ♩

   c. ♩ ♩ ♫ ♩   d. ♫ ♩ ♫ ♩

Spotlight Your Success! RESOURCE MASTER

2. **Read** these patterns using pitch syllables. Then listen. Which pattern do you hear?

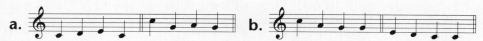

Think! Write your answers. Use your own paper

1. How is "In That Great Git'n Up Mornin'" musically the same as "Amazing Grace"?

2. What dynamics would you choose for "Reach"? Why?

3. Tell in your own words the meaning of the lyrics of "Sing, America Sing!"

4. **Write** about one piece of music from the unit. Pretend that you are hearing it for the first time. How would you describe the music using musical terms?

Create and Perform

1. Choose ♩, ♩, ♫, and 𝄽 to fill four measures in $\frac{4}{4}$ meter.

2. **Create** a melody by choosing pitches for your rhythm.
   - Use pentatonic pitches in the key of C or G.
   - If you choose C, end your melody on C. If you choose G, end your melody on G.

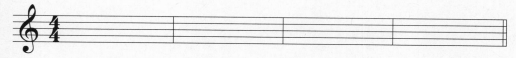

3. **Play** your melody. Use two or more dynamics as you play.

Name _____ Date _____

Self-Assessment

Who worked with you on the unit project? Write everyone's name. Tell the best thing that each person contributed to the project.

_____

_____

What did you like best about the project?

_____

What did you like least?

_____

If you could do the project again, what would you change—either about the project itself or about your work on it?

_____

How did your group do during the performance?
The goals for the project are listed below.
Put an X in the box that describes how you did.

Goal	All the way through the piece	Through most of the piece	During some of the piece	Hardly ever during the piece
Our group wrote the pitches and rhythms correctly.				
Our group played the correct rhythms and pitches.				
Our group stayed together when singing or playing our melody with the ostinatos.				

Also consider on how well your group moved between the A and B sections of the song. Circle the word or phrase that best describes the flow.

Very smooth   **Smooth**   **Somewhat smooth**   **Choppy**

Teacher Assessment RESOURCE MASTER 1•15

	Notation	Performance	Ensemble
Excellent	Consistently wrote the correct rhythm and pitches.	Consistently played the correct rhythm and pitches.	Played and sang together as an ensemble with no difficulty.
*Competent	Wrote the correct rhythm and pitches almost all of the time.	Played the correct rhythm and pitches almost all the time.	Played and sang together as an ensemble with little difficulty.
Progressing	Wrote the rhythm and pitches correctly most of the time, but with some noticeable errors.	Played the rhythm and pitches correctly most of the time, but with some noticeable errors.	Played and sang together as an ensemble with some noticeable difficulty.
Showing Little Progress	Wrote the rhythm and pitches correctly some of the time, but with many noticeable errors.	Played the rhythm and pitches correctly some of the time, but with many noticeable errors.	Played and sang together as an ensemble with a great deal of noticeable difficulty.

Not Scorable: Did not participate.

*Competent is the expected level for all students.

School-to-Home Letter

RESOURCE MASTER 2•1

Dear Family,

The theme of Unit 2 of our music curriculum is "Coming to America." In this unit, your student will be introduced to folk songs of various immigrant groups who have contributed significantly to the culture of American music. Students' understanding of basic musicology will be broadened as they deepen their awareness of different people and cultures.

In this unit your student will study new meter signatures and practice recognizing, reading, and creating different $\frac{2}{4}$ and $\frac{3}{4}$ rhythms. While learning Jewish and Zulu tunes, students will be introduced to syncopated rhythms, which they will later have a chance to practice and even create. Your student will learn two more pentatonic scales—the F and D pentatonic scales—while singing traditional Korean and Chinese folk songs. Everyone in the class will have the opportunity to grab a partner and step to the popular Italian song "Funiculi, Funicula." Also, in their exploration of traditional folk music, students will learn about some of the percussion instruments from Korea, Latin America, and Ghana.

At home you can reinforce your student's learning by sitting down with him or her and clapping out different rhythms from some of your favorite songs. Also ask your student to share the knowledge that he or she gains about different cultural groups. Spend some time learning more about these groups through reading, watching television specials, or talking with others.

Sincerely,

Fifth Grade Music Teacher

Nombre _____ Fecha _____

School-to-Home Letter

El tema de la Unidad 2 de nuestro programa musical es *"Coming to America"*. En esta unidad, su hijo conocerá las canciones autóctonas de varios grupos de inmigrantes que han contribuido de modo significativo con la cultura de la música de América. Su comprensión de la musicología básica se ampliará a medida que profundiceamos en nuestro conocimiento de los diferentes pueblos y culturas.

En esta unidad su hijo estudiará nuevas materias y practicará el reconocimiento, lectura y creación de diferentes ritmos $\frac{2}{4}$, y $\frac{3}{4}$. Mientras aprenden tonadas judías y zulúes, los alumnos conocerán los ritmos sincopados, que luego tendrán oportunidad de practicar e incluso crear. Su hijo aprenderá dos escalas pentatónicas más, la escalas F y D, mientras canta canciones folklóricas coreanas y chinas tradicionales. Tendrá la oportunidad de encontrar una pareja y zapatear al ritmo de la canción italiana *"Funiculi, Funicula"*. Además, en nuestra exploración de la música folklórica tradicional, aprenderemos algunos de los instrumentos de percusión de Corea, Latinoamérica y Ghana.

En su hogar usted puede reforzar el aprendizaje de su hijo sentándose a su lado y haciendo palmas con los distintos ritmos de algunas de sus canciones favoritas. Además, pida a su hijo o hija que comparta el conocimiento que adquiere sobre los varios grupos culturales. Pasen tiempo aprendiendo más sobre estos grupos por medio de la lectura, mirando especiales de televisión o conversando con otras personas.

Atentamente,

Maestra de Música de Quinto Grado

Creative Unit Project   RESOURCE MASTER

Your Unit 2 project gives you the opportunity to really feel the rhythm! You will write rhythm ostinatos and use them to accompany music from the unit. Then you will make your own instrument and perform an ostinato on it. Your goals are to write ostinatos that work well with specific pieces of music and to create a percussion instrument of your own. Follow the steps below.

STEP 1 *(Complete this step after studying Lesson 1 in the unit.)*
Compose the last three measures of the four-measure rhythm patterns begun below. Use these notes: ♩, ♪, ♩., ♩, ♩., 𝄽, and ▬ Try different combinations. Be careful to pay attention to the meter signature. When you are happy with your measures, notate the rhythms on the staffs below.

Practice the patterns on a drum. Then accompany "The Cliffs of Doneen" ($\frac{3}{4}$) and "Maggie in the Wood" ($\frac{4}{4}$).

STEP 2 *(Complete this step after studying Lessons 2 and 4 in the unit.)*
Practice the $\frac{3}{4}$ ostinato you composed above. Play it to accompany "Arirang." Compose other ostinatos for "Arirang," using rhythms that you know and these combinations:

As you accompany "Arirang," remember to support the melody by playing more softly than the singing. Be sure to follow the same tempo.

STEP 3 *(Complete this step after studying Lesson 3 in the unit.)*
Think about your favorite percussion instruments. What do you like about them? What makes a percussion instrument effective? Do some research on this topic. Make notes. Share your ideas with other students. Then continue thinking about percussion instruments as you answer the questions on the next page.

Creative Unit Project   RESOURCE MASTER 2·3

Brainstorm ideas about how to make your own percussion instrument.

1. How could you create a percussion instrument from found sounds (such as two rocks struck together)?

2. What materials could you use to create a percussion instrument? Some suggestions are given here, but think of your own ideas, too! (Look all the way through Unit 2 of your music book to see different instruments.)

   tambourine: bottle caps nailed to a piece of wood
   drum: overturned empty box with pencil mallets
   maracas: rice in small plastic jars

3. What instrument will you make? Write your plan on a separate sheet of paper. Include the materials you will use, and how you will make it.

4. Make your instrument. Finish it by Lesson 8.

STEP 4 (Complete this step after studying Lesson 7 in the unit.)
- Work with Resource Master 2-12. Think about the instrument you are making. With which piece of music might the sound of your percussion instrument work best?
- Cut out the rhythm cards, and arrange them to create a four-measure ostinato for the piece of music that would work best for your instrument.
- When you are happy with the astinato, notate it below. Remember to add the meter signature.

Practice the ostinato with the piece of music. Use your instrument (if it's completed), found objects, or an unpitched classroom instrument.

STEP 5 (Complete this step after completing the Unit Review.)
Demonstrate your project to the class. Use the instrument you have made. Feel the rhythm!

Practicing $\frac{3}{4}$ Meter Patterns

RESOURCE MASTER   2•4

With a partner, take turns reading and clapping the different $\frac{3}{4}$ meter patterns below. If you both have trouble with a pattern, ask a classmate or your teacher for help. The patterns become increasingly more complicated, so make sure that you both can do each pattern before continuing.

1. $\frac{3}{4}$ 1 and 2 and 3 and

2. $\frac{3}{4}$ 1 and **2 and** 3 and

3. $\frac{3}{4}$ 1 and 2 and 3 **and**

4. $\frac{3}{4}$ 1 and 2 **and** 3 and

5. $\frac{3}{4}$ 1 and 2 **and** 3 and

6. $\frac{3}{4}$ 1 and 2 **and** 3 **and**

7. $\frac{3}{4}$ 1 **and** 2 **and** 3 and

8. $\frac{3}{4}$ 1 **and** 2 **and** 3 and

9. $\frac{3}{4}$ 1 **and** 2 and 3 **and**

10. $\frac{3}{4}$ 1 **and** 2 and 3 and

Korean Percussion Instruments

RESOURCE MASTER 2•5

Write the correct instrument name next to the description that best matches it. You can use the names more than once.

jing	kkwaenaggwari	janggu	buk

_____ 1. Its two drum heads make two different sounds; one is low, and the other is high.

_____ 2. It provides the basic beat to the music.

_____ 3. It is shaped like an hourglass.

_____ 4. It is played with a stick and the left palm.

_____ 5. It is a double-headed barrel drum.

_____ 6. It has a deep, metallic sound.

_____ 7. This instrument is used to ornament the music.

_____ 8. It is played with a cloth-covered mallet.

_____ 9. It is played with a thin stick in the right hand and a mallet-shaped beater in the left.

_____ 10. It is a drum made of lacquered wood.

_____ 11. It is played with a small wood mallet that has a ball on one end.

_____ 12. It is a small metal gong.

Don't Wait— Syncopate!

RESOURCE MASTER 2•6

Clap the following rhythm, listening carefully.

It's hail - ing out - side. Ouch!

Now say each sentence below. Repeat each sentence as you clap the rhythm of "It's hail-ing out-side. Ouch!" Draw a line through any sentences that don't fit this rhythm.

I want pi-zza and fish.   The soft-ball game's all done.

Go cow - boy, get 'em. Go!   Al-li-ga-tors can bite.

Now create an interlude for "Hailing Outside." You will play "Hailing Outside" four times, then the interlude, then "Hailing Outside" four times. Choose three of the rhythm patterns below. Use one rhythm twice. Copy the rhythms into the four empty measures without placing the repeated patterns next to each other. Play your piece on a rhythm instrument.

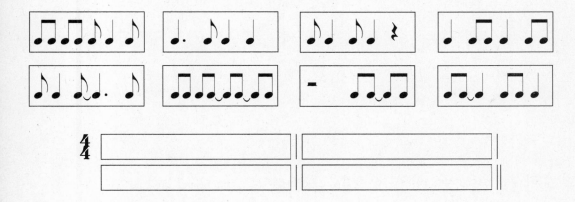

25

Name _____ Date _____

Playing with Pentatonics

1. Write the pitch syllable and pitch letter name below each note. Label each scale C, G, or F pentatonic. Sing each scale with pitch syllables.

2. a.   b.

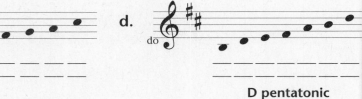

c.   d.

D pentatonic

3. Unscramble the words below. Use them to fill in the blanks in the passage about the new song you learned in this lesson. Transfer the numbered letters of the unscrambled words to the numbered blanks below the staffs. Write the pitches that match the letter names on the staffs and sing the melodies. What do you notice about the two melodies?

rewlfo	**ngya**	**gonrda**	**iheencs**	**klof**

The Fung _ _ _ _ Song is a _ _ _ _ _ _ drum song. This
         1   6   2   3

traditional _ _ _ _ _ _ _ song comes from street performers.
             7   9

This _ _ _ _ song is very old. Often, dancers perform this song
     4

wearing a _ _ _ _ _ _ costume.
          8   5 10

1   2   3   4   5   6   7   8   9   10

Name _____ Date _____

Mid-Unit Review

Match each vocabulary term or symbol to its description. Write the correct letter in the blank.

_____ 1. $\sf{\textit{d}}$.

_____ 2. harmony

_____ 3. $\mathbf{\frac{3}{4}}$

_____ 4. ornament

_____ 5. hora

_____ 6. transpose

_____ 7. klezmer

_____ 8. triple meter

_____ 9. ensemble

_____ 10. semachi rhythm

_____ 11. tie

_____ 12. syncopation

_____ 13. $\sf{\textit{J}}$.

a. three beats in a measure with a quarter note lasting one beat

b. musical style that is used to play traditional music for celebrations

c. a circle dance

d. to add extra notes to a melody

e. a musical part that supports the melody

f. equal to one and a half beats

g. musical symbol that joins two notes into a single sound

h. most common rhythm used in Korean folk music

i. the symbol for triple meter

j. equal to three beats

k. a musical group

l. to perform or write music in a key other than the one in which the music was originally written

m. rhythm in which stressed sounds occur between beats

Let's Dance to "Funiculi, Funicula!"

Many songs just beg for dancing. "Funiculi, Funicula" is one of those songs. Find a partner, form circles of four or six people, and try the dance. The song is in $\frac{6}{8}$ meter, and each measure can be counted: "1, 2."

A Section (*Measures 1–18*): Clap and snap!
Measure 1: Step right with right foot on beat 1; bring left foot next to right foot and clap hands on beat 2.
Measure 2: Step left with left foot on beat 1; bring right foot next to left foot and snap fingers on beat 2.
(Continue this way, alternating measures.)

A Section, continued (*Measures 19–36*): Swing your partner!
Measures 19–27: Partners hook right elbows and circle around each other, using skipping or jogging steps.
Measures 28–36: Partners hook left elbows and circle around each other, using skipping or jogging steps.

B Section (*Measures 37–52*): Slide, clap, and do-si-do!
Measures 37–40: Everyone hold hands and move 8 ♩♪ slides to the right.
Measures 41–44: Now move 8 ♩♪ slides to the left.
Measures 45–48: Pat thighs for 6 beats, then exchange a "high 10" (high clap with both hands) with your partner on beat 7.
Measures 49–52: Do a do-si-do (skip around your partner and back home) in 8 beats.

Interlude
Step to the beat, and find a new partner!

Let's Dance to "Funiculi, Funicula!"

After you have mastered the dance to "Funiculi, Funicula," you may enjoy a more difficult variation. It involves moving in concentric circles and changing partners. Concentric circles have a common center. In other words, one smaller circle is inside a bigger one. To start the dance, form concentric circles.

The meter is $\frac{6}{8}$.
Count it "1, 2."

A Section (*Measures 1–18*): Hop, clap, and snap!
Measure 1: Step in place with right foot on beat 1; hop on right foot and clap hands overhead on beat 2.
Measure 2: Step in place with left foot on beat 1; hop on left foot and snap fingers overhead on beat 2.

A Section, continued (*Measures 19–36*):
Swing your partner!
Measures 19–27: Partners hook right elbows and circle around each other, using skipping or jogging steps.
Measures 28–35: Partners hook left elbows and circle around each other, using skipping or jogging steps.
Measure 36: Re-form the concentric circles so that partners are facing each other.

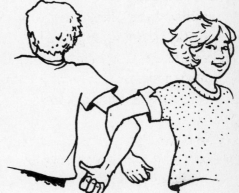

B Section (*Measures 37–52*): Circle around!
Measures 37–43: Inner circle moves to the right (clockwise) while outer circle moves to the right (counterclockwise) in a sliding sideways gallop ♩ ♪.
Measure 44: Stop in front of new partner.
Measures 45–48: Facing new partner: Pat thighs, clap own hands, clap partner's hands, clap own hands. Repeat.
Measures 49–52: Do a do-si-do with your new partner.

Interlude
Join hands with your new partner, and bounce in place to the beat.

Reviewing and Composing Rhythms

Write the correct meter signature to each of the following rhythms. Then clap and speak the rhythm. If it helps, you can write the beats out below the notes. Mark the beats that sound by underlining them.

Now compose some two-measure rhythms of your own! Write three different rhythms. Try to include some syncopation. (Do you remember syncopation? It is rhythm in which the stresses happen *between* the beats—on the "and"— instead of *on* the beats—the numbers.)

1. $\frac{2}{4}$

2. $\frac{3}{4}$

3. $\frac{4}{4}$

The Percussion of Ghana

RESOURCE MASTER 2•11

Draw a line from the instrument name to each description that fits it. You can connect each instrument to more than one description.

- shaker

- sounds like the sogo, but higher

- makes a low booming sound

Gangkogui

- has a higher- and a lower-pitched bell

Atoke

- used to play the beat

Axatse

- made from a dried gourd surrounded with strings of beads

Kidi

- double bell held in the hand and struck with a stick

Sogo

- held flat in the palm and hit with a stick

- larger version of the kidi, played with sticks while sitting

Rhythm Ostinato Cards

RESOURCE MASTER 2•12

Create a four-measure ostinato, or repeating rhythm, for one of the songs from the unit. First, choose a song to accompany.

The following songs are in $\frac{4}{4}$:
"Fung Yang Song," "Hava Nagila," "Singabahambayo," "Oye Como Va"

These songs are in $\frac{3}{4}$:
"The Cliffs of Doneen," "Arirang"

Cut out the cards at the bottom of this page, and put them together to make your ostinato. Use cards that are in the same meter as the song you choose. You must choose ♪ ♩ ♪ or ♩. ♪ as one of the rhythms.

Rearrange the cards to form different rhythm combinations. Choose your favorite combination, and use it as your ostinato. Write your ostinato in the measures below. Remember to include the meter signature.

Spotlight Your Success! RESOURCE MASTER

Review. Circle the correct answer.

1. A dotted quarter note and eighth note is written as

   a. ♩. ♩   b. ♩. ♩   c. ♩. ♪   d. ♩ ♪

2. Which of the following is a musical instrument?

   a. janggu   b. hora   c. ornament   d. tie

3. Which of the following shows syncopation without a tie?

   a. [notation]   b. [notation]   c. [notation]

4. Which of the following is an Irish musical instrument?

   a. jing   b. buk   c. kkwaenggwari   d. bodhrán

5. What is the key of this melody?

   a. G pentatonic   b. F pentatonic   c. C major   d. B minor

Read and Listen. Circle the correct answer.

1. **Read** these rhythms. Then listen. Which rhythm do you hear?

   a. [notation]   b. [notation]

2. **Read** these rhythms. Then listen. Which rhythm do you hear?

   a. [notation]   b. [notation]

   c. [notation]

Spotlight Your Success! RESOURCE MASTER

3. Read these patterns. Then listen. Which pattern shows this G pentatonic pattern transposed to F pentatonic?

Think! Write your answers. Use your own paper.

1. Name and describe at least two different styles that you heard in this unit, and name or describe two other styles that you know.

2. Name at least two percussion instruments in this unit and tell how they are alike and different.

3. How do pitch syllables or pitch letter names help you to sing pentatonic melodies?

4. Describe the texture of a song from the unit.

Create and Perform

1. **Create** a four-measure rhythm that uses ♪ ♩ ♪ and ♩. ♪ and other rhythms that you know.

2. **Write** a melody for this rhythm in G pentatonic.

3. **Transpose** your melody to F pentatonic.

4. Play your melody.

Name _____   Date _____

Self-Assessment

What type of instrument did you make for your unit project? Name and describe it. _____

Which song did you perform? _____

How well did you do in each step of the project? Rate yourself by circling the words that describe your work for each step.

	Excellent	Average	Poor
Steps 1, 2, and 4			
Writing rhythms in the correct meter	My notation had no errors.	My notation had some errors.	My notation had many errors.
Using the rhythms to accompany songs	My ostinatos sounded great with the melody.	My ostinatos sometimes did not work well with the melody.	My ostinatos did not work well with the melody.
Steps 3			
Researching effective percussion instruments	I found lots of useful information.	I found some useful information.	I found little useful information.
Brainstorming about good homemade instruments	I had lots of creative ideas.	I had some creative ideas.	I had few creative ideas.
Making the instrument	I had a detailed plan, and I followed it well.	I had a plan, but I didn't always stick to it.	I had a weak plan, and I didn't always stick to it.
Steps 5: The Performance			
Sound of instrument	My instrument had a great percussion sound.	My instrument could have had a better percussion sound.	My instrument did not have a good percussion sound.
The ostinato	The rhythm fit the song throughout, and the tempo and volume were just right.	The rhythm mostly fit the song, and the tempo and volume were appropriate much of the time.	The rhythm didn't fit the song, and the tempo and volume were not appropriate or too loud.

Name _____ Date _____

Teacher Assessment RESOURCE MASTER 2•15

	Quality of Homemade Percussion Instrument	Performance of Ostinato (Tempo)	Performance of Ostinato (Volume)
Excellent	The instrument sound had an interesting percussion tone quality that enhanced the ensemble.	Consistently played the ostinato at the same tempo as the singing throughout the song.	Enhanced the singing by playing the ostinato softer than the volume of the singing.
*Competent	The instrument made an acceptable percussion sound that blended with the others.	Played the ostinato at the same tempo as the singing through almost all of the song.	Balanced the singing by playing the ostinato at the same volume as the singing.
Progressing	The instrument made a percussion sound, but the sound detracted from the ensemble.	Played the ostinato at the same tempo as the singing through most of the song, but had occasional lapses.	Challenged the singing by playing the ostinato a little louder than the volume of the singing.
Showing Little Progress	The instrument did not have the physical properties to make a percussion sound.	Played the ostinato at the same tempo as the singing through some of the song, but struggled to keep the tempo most of the time.	Detracted from the singing by playing the ostinato too loudly to hear the singing.

Not Scorable: Did not participate.

*Competent is the expected level for all students.

Name _____ Date _____

School-to-Home Letter

Dear Family,

Change is good! That is the message of the unit your student is working on in music. Music is all about change—change in styles over the years, change when songs are arranged in new ways, change when harmonies and other accompaniments are added to enhance and transform a tune.

Musicians give music *expression* by changing the way they are playing. They vary the *tempo* (how fast the music is played); they change the *dynamics* (how loud or soft the piece is played); and they choose different types of *articulation* (how the notes are played). Composers can alter the *tone color* of a piece by having different combinations of instruments play together.

Ask your student about tempo, dynamics, articulation, and tone color. What are the names for some different ways of changing tempo? What about dynamics? What is it called when notes are connected together (*legato*) or detached (*staccato*)? Can your student demonstrate how these sound?

In this unit your student will learn several songs in $\frac{6}{8}$ meter. Have him or her sing you a song in $\frac{6}{8}$ and explain how this compound meter works. Clap along to the rhythm, and see for yourself how each beat can be divided into three parts.

Your student will also learn about major scales, intervals, and accidentals. Ask him or her to explain some terminology to you, such as half steps and whole steps, a second and a third, sharps, flats, and naturals. If you have a piano or any kind of keyboard, ask your student to use it to demonstrate.

Have fun with your student as you experiment with musical changes. Sing along to a favorite song and add a harmony. Try singing something more quietly than usual or more slowly. What other changes can you make? Remember, especially when it comes to music, change is good!

Sincerely,

Fifth Grade Music Teacher

School-to-Home Letter

Estimada Familia,

¡Es bueno cambiar! Es ése el mensaje de la unidad musical en la que está trabajando su hijo. La música es cambio—cambio en los estilos con el correr de los años, cambio cuando las canciones se arreglan de nuevas maneras, cambio cuando las armonías y otros acompañamientos se agregan para mejorar y transformar una tonada.

Incluso dentro de una sola pieza de música, existen muchos cambios. Es eso lo que hace interesante a la música. Los músicos dan la *expresión* musical cambiando el modo en que ejecutan. Cambian el *tempo* (con qué rapidez se ejecuta la música), cambian la *dinámica* (cuán fuerte o suave se ejecuta la pieza) y eligen diferentes tipos de *articulación* (cómo se tocan las notas). Los compositores pueden alterar el *color del tono* de una pieza con diferentes combinaciones de instrumentos tocados a la misma vez.

Pregúntele a su hijo sobre el tempo, la dinámica, la articulación y el color del tono. ¿Cuáles son los nombres de algunas de las diferentes maneras de cambiar el tempo? ¿Y la dinámica? ¿Cómo se dice cuando las notas están conectadas (*legato*) o separadas (*staccato*)? ¿Puede su hijo demostrar cómo suenan?

En esta unidad su hijo aprenderá varias canciones en compás de $\frac{6}{8}$. Pídale que le cante una canción en $\frac{6}{8}$ y que él le explique cómo funciona esta métrica compuesta. Palmee al son del ritmo y vea cómo cada tiempo puede dividirse en tres partes.

Su hijo también aprenderá sobre las escalas mayores, los intervalos y las accidentales. Pídale que le explique terminología, por ejemplo semi-tonos y tonos, una segunda y una tercera, sostenidas, bemoles y naturales. Si usted tiene un piano o alguna clase de teclado (incluso uno de juguete), pídale a su hijo que lo use para hacer una demostración.

Diviértase con su hijo o hija experimentando los cambios musicales. Canten una canción favorita y agreguen una armonía, o agreguen un acompañamiento con ritmo repetitivo. Hagan la prueba de cantar algo con mayor tranquilidad o lentitud de lo habitual. ¿Qué otros cambios puede hacer? Recuerde, cuando de música se trata, ¡es bueno cambiar!

Atentamente,

Maestra de Música de Quinto Grado

Name _____ Date _____

Creative Unit Project RESOURCE MASTER

Your project for Unit 3 is about transformation. When you transform something, you change it. You will work in a small group to transform a piece of music. Then you will perform your new piece! Follow the steps below to complete the transformation.

STEP 1 *(Complete this step after studying Lesson 1 in the unit.)*
One thing that you will be changing in the piece of music is the meter. Below, practice changing rhythm patterns from duple meter to compound duple meter. Write the transformed rhythms on the staves. ♩ in $\frac{2}{4}$ becomes ♩. in $\frac{6}{8}$. ♫ in $\frac{2}{4}$ becomes ♪♪♪ in $\frac{6}{8}$. 𝄽 in $\frac{2}{4}$ becomes 𝄼· in $\frac{6}{8}$. Play both patterns on body percussion or a drum.

STEP 2 *(Complete this step after studying Lesson 2 in the unit.)*
You will also transform the melody of the music. You will begin with this pentatonic melody. Play or sing it now.

Now transform the melody to diatonic by adding *fa* and *ti*. To add more notes to the rhythm, you can change ♩ to ♫; or ♩ to ♩♩, ♫♫, or ♩♪ Give each extra note either the pitch *fa* or *ti*. Notate the new melody on the next page.

Creative Unit Project   RESOURCE MASTER

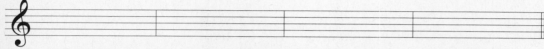

Sing or play the new diatonic melody. Add a percussion accompaniment using the duple pattern in Step 1.

STEP 3 *(Complete this step after studying Lesson 3 in the unit.)*
Now transform the rhythm of the diatonic melody. Change it from duple to compound duple. Use ♪♪♪ , ♪ , and ♩. Add repeated pitches if necessary, or even new diatonic pitches. Notate the transformed melody on the staff.

Sing or play the transformation. Add a percussion accompaniment, using the compound duple meter pattern from Step 1.

STEP 4 *(Complete this step after studying Lesson 4 in the unit.)*
Transform the three melodies even more by adding harmony. Add notes to make harmony in thirds below the melodies. Leave the beginning and ending notes to be played or sung in unison on C, *do.* Notate your final transformation on the staves in Steps 2 and 3.

Practice playing your melody and harmony parts on pitched instruments. If you use barred instruments or recorders without low A or low B, C and D should both be in unison. Add the percussion accompaniment if you like. Keep practicing until your group is ready to perform.

Name _____ Date _____

Clapping and Tapping in $\frac{6}{8}$

1. Clap these $\frac{6}{8}$ rhythms.

2. Add words to the $\frac{6}{8}$ rhythms above that you feel celebrate the United States of America. Perform your rhythmic speech pieces.

3. Compose two measures of rhythm on the staff below that you can play along with "De colores" on page 88 of your music book. The rhythm should work well with the whole song. Perform your rhythm as an ostinato with the song.

A Closer Look at "Mango Walk"

Look carefully at the notation for the song "Mango Walk."

1. On the two lines below the notes, write in the letter name of each note (top line) and the pitch syllable name (bottom line).

2. Locate a half-step interval between two notes in the song. Draw a circle around the half step. Find a whole-step interval. Put a square around the two notes that are a whole step apart.

Hardships of the Pioneer Life

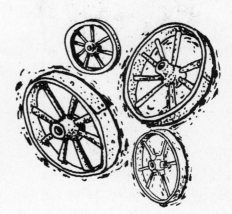

In 1862 President Lincoln signed the Homestead Act, opening up 270 million acres of land (about 10 percent of the area of the United States) for settlement. All you had to do to claim your 160-acre parcel was to be the head of a household and 21 years of age or older. If you could live there, build a house, improve the land, and farm for five years, the parcel was yours to keep.

Thousands of pioneers rushed to take up the homesteading challenge. Settlers included new immigrants, farmers from the East who had no land of their own, Civil War widows, former slaves, and many others. The land might be "free," but successfully keeping a claim required luck, skill, and hard work.

Life for the settlers was extremely difficult. They had to build their own shelters, which often were log cabins or dugouts cut into a hill. Conditions were cold in winter, hot in summer, dark, smoky, cramped, and crowded. Sometimes pioneers had to defend themselves from groups of Native Americans.

Farming meant clearing the land and working hard to raise crops. Bad weather, insects, or fire could wipe out a farmer overnight. There was always work to be done on a homestead. Getting food to eat daily involved hunting or gathering, gardening, cooking, and then preserving food for the winter. Clothes had to be made, mended, and washed by hand. Livestock needed to be looked after plus any number of other chores.

For the settlers, music was a joyful form of free entertainment. Considering all of the hardships, it is surprising how few pioneer songs grumble about the difficulties of life. Perhaps singing was a chance to escape life's everyday trials.

Make up your own funny song that laughs at or complains about the difficult things in your life.

Composing Music for a Poem

RESOURCE MASTER 3•7

Read the following poem. You will set it to your own music.

> Fiddle dee dee,
> Fiddle dee dee,
> The fly has married the bumblebee.
> They went to the church,
> And married was she.
> The fly has married the bumblebee.

Begin by notating the rhythm. Use ♪♪♪, ♩., ♪, ♩, ⁊, ♫

Think about how the rhythm of the words works in $\frac{6}{8}$ meter. Write the words below your notation.

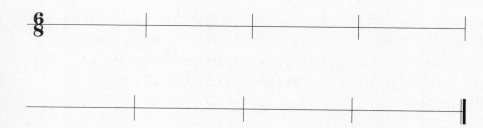

Now write a melody for the rhythm. Write your composition in C major. Once you are happy with the melody, add harmony in thirds. Write the thirds below the melody, as in "Colores de caracol."

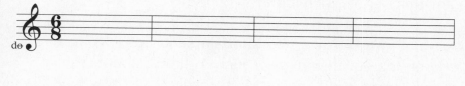

Perform your composition.

Mid-Unit Review

1. **Compound Meter.** Look at the three staves, and find the one that is in $\frac{6}{8}$. Show which one it is by writing in the meter.

2. **Half steps and whole steps.** Circle two half steps in the top staff above. Draw a box around a whole step.

3. **Accidentals.** In the third staff above, make the following changes: In the first measure, change the B to a B flat; in the second measure, make the first E an E flat and the second E an E natural; in the third measure, make the F an F sharp.

4. **Intervals.** In the first measure below, add a note to make a second. In the second measure, add a note to make a third.

Mid-Unit Review (continued)   RESOURCE MASTER   3•8

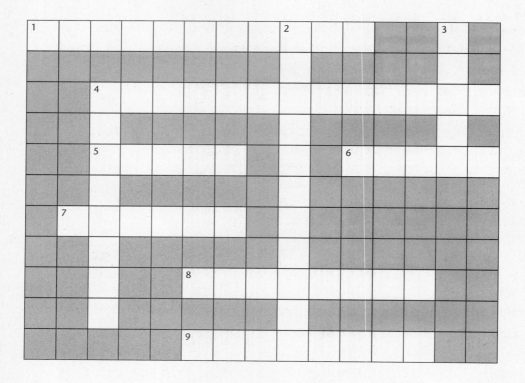

Across

1 Sharps, flats, and naturals are called _____

4 A melody that sounds good with another melody

5 A diatonic scale with *do* as the tonal center

6 $\frac{6}{8}$ is a compound _____

7 A style of religious music started by African Americans

8 The distance from one pitch to the next

9 A kind of scale that includes *do, re, mi, fa, so, la,* and *ti*

Down

2 A composer rewrites a piece of music to make an _____

3 An interval equal to two half steps

4 When beats are divided into three parts, it is a _____ meter

Moving to "Joyful, Joyful"

You can move your feet and arms to "Joyful, Joyful" from *Sister Act 2.* Follow the directions measure by measure, and get into the groove!

Measures 1 and 2 (These movements will be done twice—once per measure, on the beat.)

FEET	ARMS
Step right with your right foot.	Hold arms above left shoulder.
Touch next to your right foot with your left toes.	Cross left arm to right hip.
Step left with your left foot.	Keep right arm over left shoulder.
Touch next to your left foot with your right toes.	Cross right arm to left hip.

Measures 3 and 4

FEET	ARMS
Step right with your right foot.	Hold arms parallel to the floor.
Bring your left foot together with your right foot.	With index fingers, point to the right.
Step right with your right foot.	Hold arms parallel to the floor.
Touch next to right foot with your left toes.	With index fingers, point to the right.
Step left with your left foot.	Hold arms parallel to the floor.
Bring your right foot together with your left foot.	With index fingers, point to the left.
Step left with your left foot.	Hold arms parallel to the floor.
Touch next to left foot with your left toes.	With index fingers, point to the left.

Moving to "Joyful, Joyful"

Measures 5–8 (one movement for each measure)

FEET	ARMS
Stand in place.	Place hands on heart.
Bend knees.	Open arms up above head.
Come up on toes.	Hold arms above head, palms of hands up.
Stand in place.	Return arms to front of body, palms of hands up.

Measures 9–12 (These movements will be done four times— once per measure.)

FEET	ARMS
Step right with your right foot.	Place right index finger on left hip.
Touch next to your right foot with your left toes.	Circle right index finger to right hip.
Step left with your left foot.	Place left index finger on right hip.
Touch next to your left foot with your right toes.	Circle left index finger to left hip.

Measures 13 and 14 (repeat movements for Measures 3 and 4)
Measures 15 and 16 (repeat movements for Measures 1 and 2)
Measure 17: Stand still, holding hands in front, palms up.

Going to a Classical Music Concert

RESOURCE MASTER 3•10

If you have ever been to a classical music concert, you know that it is very different from a pop concert. At a pop concert, the audience shows its appreciation for the music by cheering and maybe even singing along. A classical concert is more like a movie, where you sit quietly and concentrate on what is going on.

Imagine an annoying person next to you at a movie who is chatting and rustling candy wrappers. You can neither hear what the actors are saying nor follow the story. The same is true for a classical concert. Sitting quietly and listening carefully are the best ways to be considerate and to show respect for the musicians.

Another feature of a classical concert is that the audience applauds at specific times. For symphonies and other works with more than one movement, it is customary *not* to clap between movements. Instead, the audience saves its applause until the end of the entire work. Check the program to see which pieces have more than one movement.

One thing that can make a classical concert more fun is becoming familiar with the music before you go. Learn which pieces will be on the program. Then check to see whether your local library has recordings. At the concert, read the information in the program about the composer and the works.

In previous times, people would always wear fancy clothes to classical concerts. Now dress codes are more relaxed. Although many people still enjoy dressing up for a concert, it's generally all right to go in casual clothes. Listening is what is most important.

Choose one of these activities:

Find out whether a classical concert is being held near you. What music will be played? Can you find a CD at your local library of at least one piece on the program?

Write a letter to your local newspaper to complain about the behavior of some people at a concert you recently attended.

Name _____ Date _____

Sorting Out Musical Terminology!

1. The words listed below describe different ways to give music expression. Explain each term in your own words.

   Tempo: _____

   Dynamics: _____

   Articulation: _____

   Tone color: _____

2. Place words from the box below under the related heading. Not all words will be used.

   Tempo   Dynamics   Articulation

   _____   _____   _____

   _____   _____   _____

   _____   _____   _____

   _____   _____   _____

   _____   _____   _____

3. Find three pairs of opposites in the box below.

   _____   is the opposite of   _____.

   _____   is the opposite of   _____.

   _____   is the opposite of   _____.

articulation	expression	dynamics	legato	tempo
accelerando	crescendo	decrescendo	staccato	ritardando
tone color	accent	rubato	fermata	a tempo

Spotlight Your Success! RESOURCE MASTER 3•12

Review. Circle the correct answer.

1. What is created when a piece of music is changed so that it has different instruments or voices from the original?

   a. a largo

   b. an arrangement

   c. a medley

2. What is the style of religious music, started by African Americans, that includes improvisation and strong feelings?

   a. gospel

   b. symphony

   c. bluegrass

3. Which diatonic scale has the tonal center of *do?*

   a. minor scale

   b. pentatonic scale

   c. major scale

4. What is the interval from one letter name to the very next letter name?

   a. third

   b. second

   c. octave

Read and Listen. Circle your answers.

1. Read these rhythms. Then listen. Which rhythm pattern is in compound meter?

Spotlight Your Success! RESOURCE MASTER 3•12

2. Read these rhythms. Then listen. Which rhythm do you hear?

a. [music notation in $\frac{6}{8}$]   b. [music notation in $\frac{6}{8}$]

3. Read these pitches. Then listen. Which pattern includes *fa* and is the diatonic C-major scale?

a. [staff notation]   b. [staff notation]

Think! Write your answers. Use your own paper.

1. How are duple and compound duple meter different?

2. Choose a song. How would it sound different without *fa* or *ti?*

3. How has "Ode to Joy" been transformed since it was created?

4. Write about a favorite musical change in this unit. What elements were changed and why was it interesting?

Create and Perform

1. **Play** or sing the C-major scale in $\frac{4}{4}$ with quarter notes.

2. **Arrange** the scale by changing it in one or more ways. You might change the tone color, rhythm, meter, tempo, or rearrange the pitches. You might add harmony, dynamics, or articulation. Notate the changed scale below.

[empty staff in $\frac{4}{4}$]

3. **Play** or sing your arrangement.

Self-Assessment

Who worked with you on the unit project? Write everyone's name. Tell the best thing that each person contributed to the project.

_____

_____

_____

What did you like best about the project? _____

_____

If you could do the project again, what would you change—either about the project itself or about your work on it? _____

_____

How difficult did your group find the various transformations? Circle the words that describe each experience.

Transforming rhythm patterns from duple meter to compound duple meter

Very difficult   **Somewhat difficult**   **Somewhat easy**   **Easy**

Transforming pentatonic melody to diatonic melody

Very difficult   **Somewhat difficult**   **Somewhat easy**   **Easy**

Transforming melody by adding harmony

Very difficult   **Somewhat difficult**   **Somewhat easy**   **Easy**

Teacher Assessment RESOURCE MASTER

	Transformation of Rhythm Patterns from Duple Meter to Compound Duple Meter	Transformation of Melody from Pentatonic to Diatonic	Transformation from Melody Alone to a Melody Harmonized in Thirds
Excellent	Transformed the duple meter rhythm pattern to compound duple rhythm pattern completely accurately.	Correctly transformed the pentatonic melody to a diatonic melody with no errors.	Transformed the melody alone to a melody harmonized in thirds without assistance.
*Competent	Transformed the duple meter rhythm pattern to compound duple rythm pattern almost accurately.	Correctly transformed the pentatonic melody to a diatonic melody with few errors.	Transformed the melody alone to a melody harmonized in thirds with minimal assistance.
Progressing	Transformed the duple meter rhythm pattern to compound duple rhythm pattern with several inaccuracies.	Transformed the pentatonic melody to a diatonic melody, but with quite a few errors.	Transformed the melody alone to a melody harmonized in thirds with moderate assistance.
Showing Little Progress	Transformed the duple meter rhythm pattern to compound duple rhythm pattern with major errors.	Transformed the pentatonic melody to a diatonic melody with many errors.	Transformed the melody alone to a melody harmonized in thirds with considerable assistance.

Not Scorable: Did not participate.

*Competent is the expected level for all students.

School-to-Home Letter

Dear Family,

The unit your student is studying in music gets off to a running start with six-teenth notes. Sixteenth notes are usually fast and exciting. Each quarter note can be divided into four sixteenths. You can make many different rhythms by putting together combinations of sixteenths and eighths. For example, two sixteenths and an eighth make one quarter note beat. It's almost like study-ing fractions!

Students will have many opportunities to practice putting together rhythms using sixteenths in various combinations. They also learn how rhythm pat-terns in a song can give or reinforce meaning. A rhythm can make a song more exciting or more peaceful. The rhythm and the lyrics work hand-in-hand with the tune to create a complete musical experience.

Another important topic covered in this unit is the difference between major and minor scales and keys. Whether a song is in a major or a minor key has a great influence on how it sounds and feels. Ask your student to sing a song in a minor key and describe the feeling. What about a song in a major key? What kind of mood does it have? Major and minor scales have different patterns of half and whole steps. Ask your student to write out the pattern for each.

Your student will encounter many new vocabulary words in this unit, such as *chord, triad, root, a cappella, ballad,* and *partner songs.* Ask for definitions and explanations. What is a chord? What is the root of the chord? What is a cap-pella singing? Ask your student to teach you a partner song, and then the whole family can try singing songs a cappella!

Sincerely,

Fifth Grade Music Teacher

School-to-Home Letter

Estimada Familia,

La unidad que está estudiando su hijo en música arranca con un rápido comienzo ya que se estudian las semicorcheas. Las semicorcheas son generalmente rápidas y emocionantes. Cada negra puede dividirse en cuatro semicorcheas. Usted puede hacer muchos ritmos diferentes al unir combinaciones de semicorcheas y corcheas. Por ejemplo, dos semicorcheas y una corchea forman un ritmo de negra. ¡Es casi como estudiar las fracciones!

Los alumnos tendrán muchas oportunidades de practicar uniendo los ritmos usando las semicorcheas en varias combinaciones. También pueden aprender cómo los esquemas de ritmo en una canción pueden dar un significado o reforzarlo. Un ritmo puede hacer que una canción sea más excitante o más pacífica. El ritmo y el trabajo de las letras trabajan 'codo a codo' con la tonada para crear una experiencia musical completa.

Otro importante aspecto cubierto en esta unidad es la diferencia entre las escalas mayores y menores y las tonalidades (claves). El hecho de que una canción esté en una clave mayor o menor tiene mucha influencia en cómo se escucha y cómo se siente. Pídale a su hijo que cante una canción en una clave menor y que describa el sentimiento. ¿Y qué pasa con una canción en clave mayor? ¿Qué tipo de 'ánimo' comunica o tiene? Las escalas mayores y menores tienen diferentes esquemas de tonos y semitonos. Pídale a su hijo que escriba los esquemas para cada uno.

Su hijo se encontrará con mucho vocabulario nuevo en esta unidad, como por ejemplo acorde, triada, raíz, a cappella, balada, y canciones a dúo. Pídale las definiciones y las explicaciones. ¿Qué es un acorde? ¿Cuál es la raíz del acorde? ¿Qué es un canto a capella? Pídale a su hijo o hija que le enseñe a cantar a dúo y luego ¡toda la familia puede intentar cantar a cappella!

Atentamente,

Maestra de Música de Quinto Grado

Creative Unit Project

RESOURCE MASTER

Your project for Unit 4 is to create and perform a musical message. You will work in a group to write ostinatos, lyrics, and a melody in two keys, and then perform your compositions. You will also decide by yourselves how to evaluate your work on the project using Resource Master 4-15. Follow the steps below.

STEP 1 *(Complete this step after studying Lesson 1 in the unit.)*
Create a two-measure $\frac{2}{4}$ ostinato. One measure should have mostly sixteenth notes. The other measure should use mostly eighth notes and/or eighth rests. Notate the measures below.

Add words to the ostinato. Use key words or phrases from "Joshua Fit the Battle of Jericho" or "Üsküdar." Fit the words to the rhythms. Practice the ostinato.

STEP 2 *(Complete this step after studying Lesson 2 in the unit.)*
Add pitches to your ostinato. First, compose the melody in the key of D minor. Use D, E, and F. Notate the ostinato below.

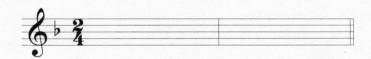

Transform the ostinato to F major. Replace the pitches above with F, G, and A. Notate the new version below. Practice the ostinato in both keys.

STEP 3 *(Complete this step after studying Lesson 4 in the unit.)*
With your group, discuss the stories of the following songs: "Joshua Fit the Battle of Jericho," "Üsküdar," "Ride Like the Wind," "Erie Canal," "Loch Lomond."

Creative Unit Project

REStOURCE MASTER

As a group, decide on your favorite story. You will write your musical message about this song. In preparation, answer these questions.

1. What is the main problem, or crisis, of the story?
2. Wo is the leading character? What is his or her role in the crisis?
3. How is the crisis resolved?

Decide on a brief message in the form of a poem or verse that the leading character will send to a friend or family member. The character should describe the crisis. List key words about the crisis. For each word, try to think of a word with a similar meaning that has either fewer or more syllables. Add rhyming words.

STEP 4 *(Complete this step after studying Lesson 5 in the unit.)*
Arrange the message to fit four measures in $\frac{2}{4}$. Notate the words or rhythm. Practice speaking the message in rhythm while patting the beat.

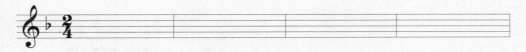

STEP 5 *(Complete this step after studying Lesson 6 in the unit.)*
Add pitches to your poem to create a melody. Work in D minor first, using D, E, F, G, and A. Write the melody on the staff. Add the lyrics below.

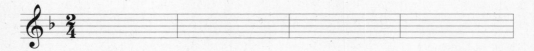

Now transform the melody to F major. Use the pitches F, G, A, B♭, and C. Write it and the lyrics below. Sing or play your song in both keys.

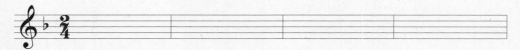

STEP 6 *(Complete this step after studying Lesson 7 in the unit.)*
Select the minor or major version that you will perform. Perform your composition.

Name _____ Date _____

Counting Sixteenths

Use this chart as a reference for various rhythms.

1. Tap out these rhythms.

2. Add notes to make two full beats in every measure. Use each of the following rhythms at least once:

3. Write your own rhythms using sixteenths.

Major and Minor

1. Fill in the missing notes and pitch names in the major scale.

do ___ mi fa ___ ___ ti ___

Use these diagrams to help you remember the whole- and half-step patterns in major and minor scales.

Major Scale

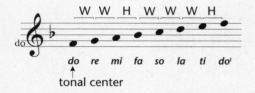

do re mi fa so la ti do'
↑ tonal center

Minor Scale

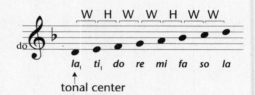

la, ti, do re mi fa so la
↑ tonal center

Look at the examples of major and minor scales below. See how the whole and half steps are the same as the whole-step and half-step patterns above.

2. To determine whether a scale is major or minor, figure out whether it starts on *do* or *la* by looking at the pattern of whole and half steps. Write *Major Scale* or *Minor Scale* in the blanks above. What is the letter name of the major scale above? You can tell by looking at the first and last notes. The scale is C major because it starts and ends on a C. What about the minor scale? What letter does it start and end on?

Write the name of the minor scale. _____

Practicing Major and Minor

1. Identify the following scales. Give the letter name, and tell whether the key is major or minor.

The two scales above have the same key signature and use the same pitches. The first scale is G major. The second one is E minor. E minor is the relative minor for G major, and G major is the relative major for E minor.

The relative minor is always three half steps down from the major: G to F#, F# to F, F to E. The relative major is three half steps up from the minor: E to F, F to F#, F# to G.

2. Fill in the blanks in the following chart with the relative minors or majors for each key given. Use the rules above to help you.

Major		Minor	Major		Minor
C Major			F Major		
		E Minor			B Minor

3. Using the major scale chart, write out a D major scale on the first staff. On the second staff, give the name of and write out its relative minor scale.

Ostinatos for Two Songs

RESOURCE MASTER 4•7

1. Use the staff below to write your four-beat ostinato for "Üsküdar" and "Joshua Fit the Battle of Jericho." Use the rhythms you found in both songs or the rhythms on page 135.

$\frac{2}{4}$

2. Use the staff below to write your quiet four-beat ostinato for the B section of "Simple Gifts." Include eighth and sixteenth patterns and other rhythms you know.

$\frac{2}{4}$

3. Compose a four-measure rhythm using these rhythm patterns.

$\frac{2}{4}$

4. Compose a two-beat ostinato to play with your rhythm above.

$\frac{2}{4}$

Story of Loch Lomond

Ballads are stories in song. Sometimes it's easy to figure out what the song is about, but sometimes it's tricky. Look at the refrain of "Loch Lomond." What is it about, exactly?

> *O, ye'll tak' the high road and I'll tak' the low road,*
> *And I'll be in Scotland afore ye,*
> *But me and my true love will never meet again,*
> *On the bonnie, bonnie banks of Loch Lomond.*

"Loch Lomond" is about two people in love who used to meet on the banks of that beautiful Scottish lake. The verses describe the place and tell how nice it was to meet there with a loved one.

Most people agree that the person singing the song is a Scottish rebel soldier who has been fighting against England. He has been captured, taken to England, and is about to be killed. That's why he and his "true love will never meet again."

What does the singer mean by the "high road" and the "low road"? The high road is the road across the mountains back to Scotland. This is the road the person who is still alive will take, walking slowly. The singer, after he is dead, will travel on an imaginary "low road" and reach home quickly, before the person who has to walk over the mountains.

Some people say that the person traveling back to Scotland on the high road is the singer's "true love." Others say that it is another rebel soldier who has been freed and is being sent home to Scotland to tell others not to fight the English. He will bring a message to the "true love" that her man has been killed.

Can you write the words to a ballad? Write about something exciting that happened to you or about the life of a famous person or hero. Write it on the back of this page.

Name _____ Date _____

Mid-Unit Review

1. Write four different one-beat rhythm patterns that include at least one sixteenth note, such as the following:

2. In the blank, write the name of this scale and tell whether it is major or minor.

 _____

3. Find the relative major or minor of the scale above. Draw the scale, and put its full name in the blank.

_____

4. Fill in each blank with the correct word from the box.

   The two notes were connected together with a _____ .

   I played all four notes together in a _____ .

   She loves to _____ when she sings.

   He added a third note to make a _____ .

   The _____ of the triad was middle C.

triad	improvise	chord	slur	root

Reviewing Meter Signatures

 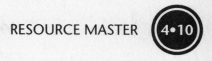

Use this chart to help you identify meter signatures.

Identify the meter in each line of music below, and write the meter signature at the beginning of the staff.

(Quarter note gets the beat.)

(Half note gets the beat.)

(Quarter note gets the beat.)

Lyrics for "Kojo No Tsuki"

RESOURCE MASTER 4•11

Look at the melody of "Kojo No Tsuki," below. Play the melody on a piano or other instrument. Would you say that the tune is mainly sad or happy, peaceful or excited? Do you think the melody goes well with the idea of a ruined castle in the moonlight? What other images and ideas does the music make you think about and feel?

Music by Rentaro Taki

Think of something in your life that matches the feeling and rhythm of "Kojo No Tsuki." Make up lyrics about your experience that you can sing to this melody. Write two verses of your song underneath the lines of music above. Write any additional verses on the back of this page.

What instrument or instruments would you choose to play your song? Explain your choice.

_____

_____

Name _____ Date _____

Martha Graham

Styles in art change over time—sometimes slowly and sometimes quickly when an artist has bold new ideas. Change is important. Think about changes in music. What if styles had not changed at all in the last 150 years? What kinds of music would you miss?

Aaron Copland was a musical innovator. Martha Graham, the choreographer of "Appalachian Spring," was a dance revolutionary. She was not the first to break away from the strict rules and traditions of ballet, but she was the most important person in the creation of a new form of movement called modern dance, a style based on dance as a means of creative expression.

Graham was born in Pittsburgh in 1894. She did not start her dance training until she was 22—very late for an aspiring dancer. After dancing in someone else's company, she went out on her own in 1923. By the 1940s she had won nationwide recognition and acclaim with dances such as "Letter to the World."

Graham's dances looked nothing like ballet. They were filled with strong emotions such as fear, joy, and jealousy. She danced with raw power in a way that was totally new. Some people found it exciting. Others found it shocking.

Graham was an extraordinary dancer, but she was also important as a teacher and choreographer. She danced until she was 75 (and lived to 97), but her dances and training technique have lived even longer. The dances are still performed today, and many young dancers are trained using her technique.

Many of the men and women who danced with Graham went on to start their own companies. Modern dance began to grow and change and become even more varied. Today there are hundreds of modern dance companies all around the world.

Write a one-sentence summary of what you believe to be Martha Graham's greatest accomplishment. Use your own paper.

Partner Songs

Partner songs like the variants of "Follow the Drinkin' Gourd" and "Wade in the Water" sound good when they are sung together. What are other ways to sing in parts? What about rounds? Do you know "Three Blind Mice" and "Row, Row, Row Your Boat"? Each of these rounds is fun to sing on its own, with singers coming in at the beginning of each section until all four sections are being sung at the same time.

For even more fun, try singing both rounds together! The rounds are in the same key and have the same meter signature, so everything fits. Rounds and partner songs are two ways of singing together. Now sing these other ways with a partner.

1. Sing this echo song together, and then make up your own echo song.

2. Part B is a harmony one third above Part A. Sing the parts together, and then make up your own melody and harmony to sing together in thirds.

3. These two independent parts fit nicely. Sing them together.

Name _____ Date _____

Spotlight Your Success! RESOURCE MASTER

Review. Circle the correct answer.

1. What note values are in this rhythm? ♩ ♫

   a. half, quarter, quarter

   b. eighth, sixteenth, sixteenth

   c. dotted eighth, sixteenth, whole

2. How many sixteenth notes fit in one quarter note?

   a. 2   c. 4

   b. 3   d. 16

3. What kind of chord is made up of three pitches?

   a. root   b. chord pattern   c. triad

4. What kind of key has half steps between steps 2 and 3 and 5 and 6?

   a. minor   c. major

   b. pentatonic   d. tonal

5. Which chord is minor?

   a. *do mi so*   b. *la do mi*   c. *fa la do*

Read and Listen. Circle the correct answer.

1. **Read** these rhythms. Then listen. Which rhythm do you hear?

2. **Read** these rhythms. Then listen. Which rhythm do you hear?

Spotlight Your Success! RESOURCE MASTER

3. Read these pitches. Then listen. Which scale is minor?

   a. *do re mi fa so la ti do'*

   b. *la, ti, do re mi fa so la*

   c. *so la do re mi so' la' do'*

Think! Write your answers. Use your own paper.

1. What is the difference between a ballad and a ballet?

2. Can you sing a triad with others? How did that make you feel?

3. What uses could you find for relative minor and relative major keys?

4. Choose a story song and tell its story in your own words.

Create and Perform

1. Choose a major or minor triad.

2. **Create** an eight-beat rhythm that uses at least two sixteenth-note patterns.

3. Select pitches from your triad for the rhythm. Notate your piece.

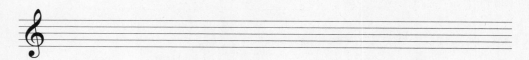

4. **Play** or sing your piece.

Name ____________________ Date ____________________

Self-Assessment

RESOURCE MASTER 4•15

Your group will get to decide for yourselves some of the things you will be evaluated on for this project. During the project, you should fill in the blanks in the chart below. Decide what would make your work *excellent, average,* or *poor.* Follow the example given for the evaluation of the lyrics you write.

	Excellent	**Average**	**Poor**
Lyrics	The lyrics make the song's crisis really come to life.	The lyrics describe the song's crisis in a clear way.	The lyrics do not describe the song's crisis well.
Ostinato			
Melody			

One you complete your project, circle the words in the chart above that describe how you did. Then answer the questions that follow.

What did you like best about the project? ____________________

____

If you could do the project again, what would you change—either about the project itself or about your work on it? ____________________

____

Teacher Assessment   RESOURCE MASTER 4•16

	Lyrics	Expression	Stage Presence
Excellent	Lyrics relate to the meaning of the original song and rhymed.	Used engaging expression in voice and face to interpret the meaning of the lyrics.	Performed with a great deal of energy, focus, and confidence.
***Competent**	Lyrics were related to the meaning of the original song and might have a rhyme.	Used appropriate expression in voice and face to convey the meaning of the lyrics.	Performed with noticeable energy, focus, and confidence.
Progressing	Lyrics were somewhat related to the meaning of the original song.	Attempted to use some expression in voice and face to show the meaning of the lyrics.	Performed with some energy, focus, and confidence.
Showing Little Progress	Lyrics did not relate to the meaning of the original song.	Did not attempt to use expression in voice and face to show the meaning of the lyrics.	Performed with little energy, focus, and/or confidence.

Not Scorable: Did not participate.

***Competent is the expected level for all students.**

Name _____ Date _____

School-to-Home Letter

Dear Family,

The musical journey through the world continues in Unit 5 of our music curriculum. On the way, students stop and learn new musical terms, forms, and styles and develop their understanding of more cultures and peoples.

The first unit introduces chords via the music of the Caribbean. Students will learn the difference between tonic, dominant, and subdominant E chords and how they are used to accompany songs. Students will further their understanding of chords while learning a Jewish song celebrating the creation of Israel and a popular song that originated in Africa.

The American blues is the medium through which students will study chord progressions and improvisation. Your student will even get the chance to improvise a song of his or her own! Students will study musical form with a Mexican tune and dance to a Swedish folk song.

As you can see, students are in for another fun and exciting musical adventure. Thank you so much for any assistance you have already afforded me: at home, at school, or both. Anything more you can offer this year is greatly appreciated. Together we can create a musical learning experience for your student that will enrich his or her life for many years to come.

Sincerely,

Fifth Grade Music Teacher

School-to-Home Letter

Estimada Familia,

El viaje musical alrededor del mundo continúa en la Unidad 5 de nuestro programa musical. En la ruta, los alumnos se detienen y aprendes nuevos términos musicales, estructuras y estilos y desarrollan su comprensión de otras culturas y otros pueblos.

La primera unidad presenta los acordes por medio de la música del Caribe. Su hijo aprenderá las diferencias entre los acordes tónicos, dominantes y subdominantes y cómo se utilizan para acompañar las canciones. Los alumnos profundizarán su conocimiento sobre acordes mientras aprenden una canción judía que celebra la creación de Israel. El *blues* Americano servirá para que los alumnos estudien las progresiones de acordes y la improvisación. ¡Incluso su hijo tendrá la oportunidad de improvisar una canción propia! Estudiaremos la forma musical con una tonada mexicana y danzaremos al ritmo de una canción folklórica sueca. Como puede ver, los alumnos tendrán otra aventura musical divertida y excitante.

Muchísimas gracias por la colaboración que ya me ha ofrecido, desde su hogar, en la escuela o en ambos lugares. Agradecemos toda otra colaboración que pueda ofrecer durante este año. Juntos podemos crear una experiencia musical de aprendizaje para su hijo o hija que enriquecerá su vida en los años venideros.

Atentamente,

Maestra de Música de Quinto Grado

Name _____ Date _____

Creative Unit Project   RESOURCE MASTER

You will complete the Unit 5 project in a group of six students. Your goals are:

- To create an accompaniment for a song using primary chords.
- To use a chord progression as a basis for a scat improvisation accompaniment.
- To use a rhythm pattern for the accompaniment that works with the song.

Follow the steps below.

STEP 1 *(Complete this step after studying Lesson 1 in the unit.)*
Choose a partner. Together, practice playing chords in the key of C. Use resonator bells, keyboards, or Orff barred instruments. Start with the I chord. Play *do* and *so* together. Then add *mi* to form the triad. Now play the I chord as a broken chord—one note at a time, *do, mi,* and *so.* Next, play the IV chord. Start with *fa* and *do'.* Then form the triad with *la.* Remember to play the broken chord. Finally, play the V chord. Play *so* with *re',* and then add *ti* for the triad. Play the broken chord. Practice with all three broken triads until you are comfortable playing them in this way.

STEP 2 *(Complete this step after studying Lesson 2 in the unit.)*
Now practice the I, IV, and V chords for the key of C major on a keyboard. (The I chord has C as its root. The IV chord has F as its root. The V chord has G as its root.) Assign one of the chords to each pair of students in your group. Practice playing the chords as broken triads. Then play the chords with "Tzena, Tzena." Match the meter of the song. Follow the chord notations to know when to play each triad.

STEP 3 *(Complete this step after studying Lesson 3 in the unit.)*
You will now work on an accompaniment to "The Lion Sleeps Tonight." This song is in G major, so you should identify the roots and triads of the I, IV, and V chords for this key. Work on a keyboard with your group to find the chords. Practice the chords with the song. Then have one group member play the root of each chord while the other group members sing the pitches of the chord. Use a rhythm pattern that fits the song's meter but does not duplicate the rhythm of the words.

Creative Unit Project   RESOURCE MASTER   5•3

STEP 4 (*Complete this step after studying Lesson 4 in the unit.*)
Organize the accompaniment you have been working on. Use pitched instruments. Follow a chord progression using all three chords in the key of F. Remember to use all the pitches from each chord. Choose a rhythm that works with the song.

STEP 5 (*Complete this step after studying Lesson 6 in the unit.*)
Practice again the accompaniment you created in Step 4. Assign keyboard and pitched instrument parts to the group members. Add a new part— scat syllables. Have a singer scat over the chord progression. Try using these syllables: *Za-za-zu-zay, Bop-du-wop, Du-ba-du-dah.* Experiment with your own syllables, too! Let everyone in the group try the different parts until you achieve the best sound. Your goal is to be relaxed in your performance.

STEP 6 (*Complete this step after studying Lesson 8 in the unit.*)
Continue practicing your chords and improvisation. Create a second improvisation. Perform your piece as an A B A C A rondo with the song as the A section and the improvisations as the B and C sections. Remember that everyone in the group should pay attention to the chord roots and the rhythm. Everyone must be on pitch and in rhythm, but people watching your performance should see that you are free and at ease. When you are ready, make a plan to present your performance.

The Main Chord

You can accompany most songs knowing only the three primary chords of its key: the I chord, built on the first step of the scale, *do;* the IV chord, built on the fourth step of the scale, *fa;* and the V chord, built on the fifth step of the scale, *so.* Look at the keyboard below, and shade or highlight the C-major scale.

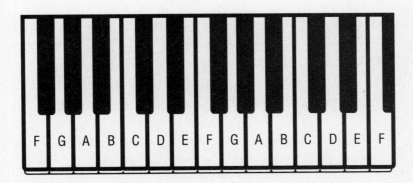

1. In the key of C major, the I chord is built on the pitch _____.

2. In the key of C major, the IV chord is built on the pitch _____.

3. In the key of C major, the V chord is built on the pitch _____.

4. The I chord is made up of *do, mi,* and *so* (the first, third, and fifth pitches of a scale). The IV chord is made up of *fa, la,* and *do^l* (the fourth, sixth, and first steps of a scale). The V chord is made up of *so, ti,* and *re^l* (the fifth, seventh, and second steps of a scale). Look at the keyboard again. On the staff below, circle each note of the I chord in C major. Then draw a triangle around each note of the IV chord and a box around each note of the V chord.

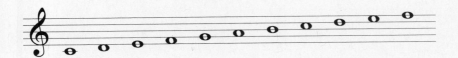

The Main Chord

Now that you know the I, IV, and V chords in C major, you can accompany songs in the key of C. Look at "Cuando salí de Cuba" in your textbook. Notice the chord symbols C, F, and G above the melody. Write the chords on the staff below in half notes. (Two measures have been done for you). Play your accompaniment on a chordal instrument as you sing the song.

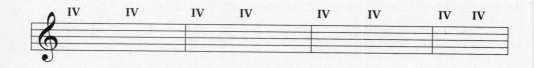

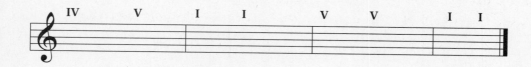

78

The Creation of Israel RESOURCE MASTER 5•5

Read about the history of Israel. Then answer the questions that follow.

The nation of Israel was established in 1948 after nearly a century of political action by Jews the world over. It was created by the United Nations following World War II as a home for all Jewish people to live free from persecution. Because of land ownership problems, its creation has been a very controversial subject.

Before the establishment of Israel, the Jews were without a home of their own. Since ancient times, they have lived in countries throughout the world as immigrants and minority groups. They have often been persecuted by other groups for who they are and what they believe. Many Jews wanted to return to the ancestral lands that they were once forced to leave. This land was called Palestine, and the people who wanted to create a Jewish state there were called Zionists.

In 1897 Jews from all over the world met at the first World Zionist Congress. They started the Zionist movement for a homeland in Palestine. At this time, Palestine was controlled by Turkey. The Turkish sultan did not want to give the land to the Jews. However, Turkey was soon involved in World War I, fighting Britain. Britain won, and in 1917 the British government promised to establish a national home for the Jews in Palestine.

Many Jews started moving to Palestine. The Arabs did not like Jews coming to live on the land, so they started fighting the Jewish occupation. This situation continued until after World War II. The Jewish people desperately needed a homeland, yet fighting between the Arabs and Jews in Palestine was increasing. In 1948 the United Nations stepped in and created the nation of Israel. For the first time in more than 2,000 years, the Jewish people had their own country.

The song "Tzena Tzena" was written to celebrate the newly created nation of Israel. What do the lyrics tell you about the feelings of the Jewish people at this time? _____

_____

Blues of "Backwater Blues"

RESOURCE MASTER 5•6

The blues sound is created by using special pitches called *blue notes*. These are pitches that have been lowered and usually have an accidental (♯, ♭, ♮) next to them. Look at the music for "Backwater Blues" in your textbook. Write the blue notes you find on the staves below that correspond to the correct measure in the song. Remember that not every accidental means a blue note.

The 12-bar blues pattern is another feature of blues music. It typically follows the chord progression: I I I I   IV IV I I   V IV I I. Identify the chords that make up the 12-bar blues pattern for "Backwater Blues." Fill in the chords in the measures below.

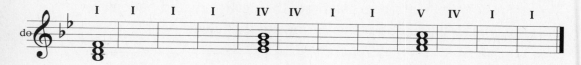

Name _____ Date _____

Singin' the Blues

Using your textbook, sing the first three lines of "Every Day I Have the Blues," paying attention to the rhythm of the music. Following the rhythm and the rhyme of the words, write lyrics for the fourth line of music in the space below. End on a word that rhymes with *blues*.

Then write the lyrics to the last line after singing the two lines starting with "Nobody loves me." Again, follow the rhythm and rhyme of the section. End on a word that rhymes with *care*.

_____

_____

_____

_____

_____

_____

_____

_____

Name _____ Date _____

Mid-Unit Review

Match each vocabulary term or symbol to its description. Write the correct letter in the blank.

_____ **1.** primary chords

_____ **2.** inversion

_____ **3.** tonic chord

_____ **4.** root position

_____ **5.** V

_____ **6.** common tones

_____ **7.** IV

_____ **8.** subdominant chord

a. a chord in which the root is not at the bottom

b. the dominant chord

c. a key's main chords: I, IV, and V

d. the subdominant chord

e. a chord built in the order root, third, fifth

f. pitches used in more than one chord

g. a chord built in the order fourth, sixth, first

h. a chord starting on the first pitch of the major scale

Label the chords below as either I, IV, V, root position (R), 1st inversion (1st), or 2nd inversion (2nd). For I, IV, and V chords, write the root's pitch name in the brackets. The first one on each staff has been done for you.

I,R [C] __[ ] __[ ] __[ ] __[ ]

IV,R [C] __[ ] __[ ] __[ ] __[ ]

Name _____ Date _____

Improving Your Improv

Use this sheet with page 182 of your music book to record your pitch, rhythm, and lyric improvisations for "Every Day I Have the Blues."

F blues scale

On the staff below, write pitches you would like to use for your improvisation.

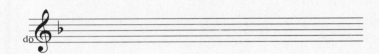

Improvise some melodies you could play or sing at the end of each phrase in "Every Day I Have the Blues." Write them down.

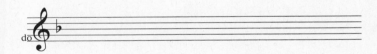

Now try making a rhythm (or rhythms) to go with your improvised melodies. Make them the same length as the one below.

Write your rhythms here.

You're now ready to perform "Every Day I Have the Blues." Use the melody and rhythm you improvised here and the lyrics you made up in Lesson 4, or you can use scat syllables such as *du dut-en dut*. Practice your version of the song until you can play it without mistakes. Then perform it in front of the class.

Name _____ Date _____

Perform the Forms

RESOURCE MASTER   5•10

Use any of the note values you have studied to create eight-beat phrases, and then write them in the boxes below. There are two A patterns, two B patterns, one A' pattern, and one B' pattern. Both A patterns should be the same, as should both B patterns. Make the A' pattern similar to the A pattern and the B' pattern similar to the B pattern.

When you are finished, use scissors to cut the boxes along the lines, making six cards. Rearrange your cards in various orders, such as A B A, A B B A, A A B A', A B A B, or A B A' B'. Form groups, and take turns performing the forms for one another. If you are not performing, guess what the form is. When your turn comes up a second time, perform a new form. (To turn this activity into a game, add a scoring system. The first person to guess a form correctly gets one point. The first player with five points wins.)

A	A
$\frac{4}{4}$	$\frac{4}{4}$

B	B
$\frac{4}{4}$	$\frac{4}{4}$

A'	B'
$\frac{4}{4}$	$\frac{4}{4}$

Stepping Swedish Style

Let's dance to "Och Jungfrun Hon Går I Ringen"! There are two sections.

The A section of the dance is performed for the first 8 measures, for 24 counts. To get started, find a partner. Partners stand side-by-side to form a double circle (one circle inside the other), facing counterclockwise. Partners join hands in a skater's hold—left hands clasped under the inside partner's right arm.

The dance follows a six-count, two-measure repeated step.

Dance Steps:	1	2	3	4	5	6
Beat	♩	♩	♩	♩	♩	♩
Foot	L	R	R	L	R	L
Step	step	close	hop*	step	close	step

* R foot behind L foot

As couples, move forward and diagonally left, *toward* the center of the circle, with each step.

Next, repeat the above step pattern, except begin with the right foot. Move diagonally forward and *away* from the center of the circle.

Do this 12-count pattern twice.

(For a fancy added feature, the second time you do the 12-count pattern, the boy, or inside partner, may raise his right arm and release the left-hand hold as the girl, or outside partner, turns clockwise passing under the boy's arm while traveling around him. This takes 12 beats.)

Stepping Swedish Style

The B section for the "Och Jungfrun Hon Går I Ringen" dance is performed during the last eight measures of the song. For this section, stand face-to-face with your partner so that the boy, or inside partner, now has his back to the center of the circle. Hold hands, left to left and right to right, so that they are crossed between you.

Now you're ready for the dance!

Dance Steps:	1		2	3
Beat	♩		♩	♩
Foot	L		R	hold
Step	step toward partner		touch	—

Dance Steps:	4		5	6
Beat	♩		♩	♩
Foot	R		L	hold
Step	step away from partner		touch	—

Next, repeat the above step pattern, except begin with the right foot.

Do this 12-count pattern twice. Then return to the side-by-side beginning position, ready to start the dance again at the A section.

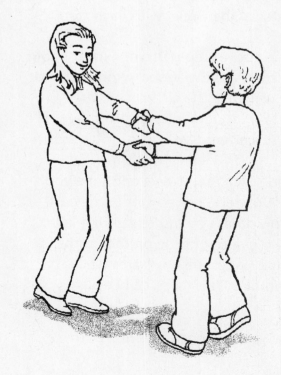

Spotlight Your Success! RESOURCE MASTER 5•12

Review. Circle the correct answer.

1. Which chord symbols represent moving from the tonic to the dominant chords?

   a. V I   **b.** IV I   **c.** I V   **d.** I IV

2. What chords are shown here?

   a. IV V I   **b.** I IV V   **c.** V I IV   **d.** IV I V

3. Which group of chords contains only primary chords?

   a. I ii IV V   **b.** I ii iii V   **c.** IV V vii   **d.** I IV V

4. Which chords are inverted?

   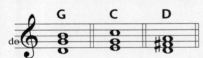

   a. G and C chords   **b.** C and D chords   **c.** G and D chord

5. Which of the following is a blues scale?

   a.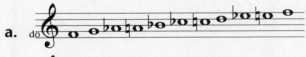

   b.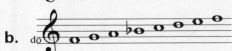

Read and Listen. Circle the correct answer.

1. Read these pitches. Then listen. Which pitches do you hear?

   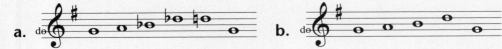

Spotlight Your Success! RESOURCE MASTER

2. Read these pitches. Then listen. Which chord do you hear?

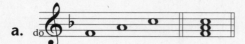 

Think! Write your answers. Use your own paper.

1. Choose a song. What would happen if different chords were used in the accompaniment?

2. Which do you think is easier to sing—legato or staccato? Why?

3. What are your favorite tone colors? Explain why.

4. Why do you think the 12-bar blues form is popular?

Create and Perform

1. **Create** a 12-bar blues melody to these words:

   I lost my homework, I feel so awful blue.
   I lost my homework, I feel so awful blue.
   Did anybody find it? I don't know what to do.

2. **Use** the pitches in the F-blues scale. Notate your melody below.

3. Sing your melody over the 12-bar blues chord progression in the key of F.

Name _____ Date _____

Self-Assessment

RESOURCE MASTER 5•13

Who worked with you on the unit project? Write everyone's name. Tell the best thing that each person contributed to the project.

_____

_____

_____

What did you like best about the project? _____

_____

What did you like least? _____

_____

If you could do the project again, what would you change—either about the project itself or about your work on it? _____

_____

How did your group do during the performance?
The goals for the project are listed below.
Put an X in the box that describes how you did.

Goal	All the way through the performance	Through most of the performance	During some of the performance	Hardly ever during the performance
Our chord progressions, melody, and improvisations fit together.				
Our group played the correct rhythm at the right tempo.				
Our group was relaxed, making the improvisation seem free and easy.				

Teacher Assessment RESOURCE MASTER 5•14

	Accompaniment/ Scat Singing	Rhythm Pattern	Style
Excellent	Matched all of the chord changes with no hesitation when accompanying or singing.	Rhythm pattern fit with the song's meter throughout the entire performance.	Performed with a highly effective free and relaxed style that seemed natural and effortless.
*Competent	Matched almost all of the chord changes without much hesitation when accompanying or singing.	Rhythm pattern fit with the song's meter throughout most of the performance.	Performed with an effective free and relaxed style that, at times, seemed natural and effortless.
Progressing	Matched most of the chord changes, but with some noticeable hesitation.	Rhythm pattern fit with the song's meter during some of the performance.	Performed with a moderately effective free and relaxed style, but effort was apparent.
Showing Little Progress	Matched some of the chord changes, but with a lot of hesitation and/or stopping.	Rhythm pattern fit with the song's meter during a little of the performance.	Performed with an attempt at a free and relaxed style that was ineffective.

Not Scorable: Did not participate.

*Competent is the expected level for all students.

Name _____ Date _____

School-to-Home Letter

Dear Family,

Unit 6 of our music curriculum focuses on the meter of music. Most American music is written in $\frac{2}{4}$, $\frac{3}{4}$, $\frac{4}{4}$, and $\frac{6}{8}$ meters, but we will also listen to irregular meters with beats organized into groups of 5 or 7. Students will sing a Spanish folk song in $\frac{3}{8}$ meter, listen for beat groupings in $\frac{5}{8}$ meter, and explore the $\frac{5}{4}$ meter made famous by the Dave Brubeck Quartet.

In this unit students will discover that some musical phrases begin with an upbeat and learn that the downbeat is the strong beat at the beginning of a measure. Students will learn about changing meters within a composition. As we listen to a Spanish folk song and chamber music by Richard Gill, we will listen for meters. Students will explore some unusual meters that are common in other parts of the world, such as $\frac{7}{4}$ and $\frac{7}{8}$ from Eastern Europe.

Later in this unit, students will enter the musical world of Native Americans. Students will learn the locations of various Indian nations through a map and develop an understanding of dance movements through the "Alligator Dance" and "Jóó Ashílá."

Students are becoming increasingly aware that each voice and instrument has its own tone color and sound. Students will explore the tone color of various chamber ensembles and orchestral percussion instruments. They will learn how to improve their own singing voices through good posture, diction, and breathing technique. Students will use a rubric to evaluate their own singing as well as the performances of others.

Unit 6 closes with "We Want to Sing" and prompts students to think about the message each wants to share with the world. Share your favorite songs and dances with your student, perhaps from other time periods or other countries. Take out your own clarinet or guitar! Enjoy your student's musical journey.

Sincerely,

Fifth Grade Music Teacher

School-to-Home Letter

Estimada Familia,

La unidad 6 de nuestro programa musical se concentra en la métrica de la música. La mayor parte de la música americana está escrita según la métrica $\frac{2}{4}$, $\frac{3}{4}$, $\frac{4}{4}$, y $\frac{6}{8}$, pero también escucharemos métricas irregulares con compases organizados en grupos de 5 ó 7. Los alumnos cantarán una canción folklórica española en métrica $\frac{3}{8}$, escucharán agrupaciones de compases en métrica $\frac{5}{8}$, y explorarán la métrica $\frac{5}{4}$, métrica que hiciera famosa el Dave Brubeck Quartet.

En esta unidad los alumnos descubrirán que algunos fraseos musicales comienzan con un tiempo no acentuado, si bien el tiempo acentuado es el tono acentuado al comienzo de un compás. Los alumnos aprenderán sobre los cambios de métrica dentro de una composición. Al escuchar la canción folkórica española y música de cámara por Richard Gill, trataremos de distinguir las diferentes métricas. Los alumnos explorarán algunas métricas que son comunes en otros lugares del mundo, por ejemplo el $\frac{7}{4}$ y $\frac{7}{8}$ de la Europa Oriental.

Al avanzar la unidad, los alumnos ingresarán al mundo musical de los indios americanos. Los alumnos aprenderán la ubicación de varias naciones indias en un mapa y desarrollarán la comprensión de los movimientos de la danza con "Alligator Dance" y "Jóó Ashílá."

La unidad 6 cierra con "We Want to Sing" e invita a los alumnos a pensar en el mensaje que cada uno quiere compartir con el mundo. Comparta sus canciones y danzas favoritas con su hijo, incluso las de otros tiempos o de otros países. ¡Desempolve su propio clarinete o su guitarra! Disfrute el viaje musical de su hijo o hija a través.

Atentamente,

Maestra de Música de Quinto Grado

Creative Unit Project RESOURCE MASTER 6•2

You will prepare and perform a concert of songs for your Unit 6 project. In a small group, you will decide how to make your concert special. Your teacher may assign you a specific song to learn. Work with a checklist of items on which your performance will be evaluated (Resource Master 6-3). This will help you to strive toward excellence in the areas that count.

STEP 1 (Complete this step after studying Lesson 1 in the unit.)
Discuss with your group the checklist on Resource Master 6-3. As you work on the songs for the concert, you will want to do the best you can in each area. Use the checklist for every song you practice. When most of the boxes are checked off to your group's satisfaction, work on the next song. Start with the three songs from the unit so far: "The Times They Are A-Changin'," "Dance for the Nations," and "Turn the World Around."

STEP 2 (Complete this step after studying Lesson 2 in the unit.)
Continue practicing the songs from Step 1. Focus on the areas that you have not yet checked off on the list. If you feel comfortable with your progress on the first three songs, also begin to work on "El vito."

STEP 3 (Complete this step after studying Lesson 3 in the unit.)
Now work on "Guantanamera" and "No despiertes a mi niño." If you have Spanish-speaking students in your group, have them help other group members with pronunciation. Use the recorded Pronunciation and IPA to help you. Be careful to express the meaning of each song.

STEP 4 (Complete this step after studying Lesson 4 in the unit.)
The next song to work on is "Shope, Shope." As a class, discuss the challenges of this song. In your group, make a plan to conquer those challenges!

STEP 5 (Complete this step after studying Lesson 6 in the unit.)
Your teacher will assign your group an instrumental accompaniment to work on for one of these songs: "Turn the World Around," "Dance for the Nations," or "El vito." You will also be working on the dance moves for "Dance for the Nations" or create movement for songs.

STEP 6 (Complete this step after studying Lesson 7 in the unit.)
The whole class will work together on the closing song for the program—"We Want to Sing" or "What the World Needs Now." Now is the time to put the whole program together. Complete any special touches. Videotape or record your rehearsal, and evaluate your work.

Name _____ Date _____

Creative Unit Project

RESOURCE MASTER 6•3

STEP 7 *(Complete this step after studying Lesson 8 in the unit.)*
Review your piece(s) and prepare a verbal introduction to each piece.
You may wish to invite an audience to attend your performance.

Performance Song Checklist

Song Title: _____

When you are satisfied with your group's progress in each area, put a check
in the box. Make notes about any special ideas in the "Comments" section.

Goals	Comments
☐ **Rhythm:** Our group stays together and matches the song's meter throughout the song.	
☐ **Pitch:** Our group stays on pitch throughout the song.	
☐ **Phrasing:** We use effective breathing to allow us to complete musical phrases smoothly.	
☐ **Vocal Tone:** Our individual and combined voices have a rich quality to them; no one is straining to hit notes.	
☐ **Use of Dynamics and Tempo:** Our group uses dynamics and tempo changes effectively.	
☐ **Posture:** We are sitting or standing tall, but we are not stiff.	
☐ **Body Language:** Our posture, facial expressions, and gestures all support the song's meaning.	
☐ **Energy:** We look and sound lively.	
☐ **Expression:** The emotions of the song come through in our performance.	
☐ **Intensity:** Our group is very focused, and we are projecting our voices well.	
☐ **Memorization:** We know all of the lyrics, pitches, and rhythms of the song by heart.	

Name _____ Date _____

Identifying Meter Signatures

Write in the correct meter signatures for the following songs. Identify whether each set of measures is in $\frac{2}{4}$, $\frac{3}{4}$, $\frac{4}{4}$, $\frac{6}{8}$, or the irregular $\frac{5}{8}$ meter. Sing the melody, and try to identify each song. Write the name on the blank line below the staff.

1.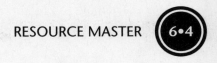

   Meter: _____ Title: _____

2.

   Meter: _____ Title: _____

3.

   Meter: _____ Title: _____

4.

   Meter: _____ Title: _____

5.

   Meter: _____ Title: _____

Downbeats and Upbeats

The **downbeat** is the first beat of a measure. The downbeat often is the strongest beat, where the "weight," or emphasis, falls. Often it marks the beginning of a musical phrase. But sometimes musical phrases begin on an upbeat.

An **upbeat** occurs just before a downbeat. It is often called a weak beat, and an upbeat leads into the downbeat. For example, in "The Star-Spangled Banner," the opening word, *Oh,* comes on the upbeat to the first measure, and *say* comes on the downbeat. Sometimes the upbeat is referred to as a pickup. One musician might ask another, "Do I have a pickup at the beginning, or do I start on the downbeat?"

The Star-Spangled Banner
(National Anthem)

Words by Francis Scott Key
Music Attributed to John Stafford Smith

Mark whether the following examples begin with an upbeat or a downbeat. Circle the upbeats. Underline the downbeats.

1.
2.
3.
4.
5.
6.

Name ______________________ Date ______________

Using Different Meter Signatures

RESOURCE MASTER 6•6

Remember that in any meter signature, the top number tells you how many beats are in a measure, and the bottom number indicates what kind of note gets one beat. A **4** on the bottom, for example, refers to a quarter note.

For each of the following meter signatures, create a rhythm that is three measures long.

$\frac{3}{8}$ | ‖

$\frac{7}{8}$ | ‖

$\frac{5}{4}$ | ‖

$\frac{6}{4}$ | ‖

$\frac{7}{4}$ | ‖

Name _____ Date _____

Mid-Unit Review

RESOURCE MASTER 6•7

Match the correct symbol or definition from the right-hand column to its vocabulary term in the left column. Write the letter in the blank.

_____ 1. downbeat

_____ 2. common time

_____ 3. irregular meter

_____ 4. upbeat

_____ 5. meter signature's bottom number

_____ 6. meter signature's top number

_____ 7. meter

_____ 8. chamber music

_____ 9. changing meters

_____ 10. "Guantanamera"

a. a song from Spain

b. $\frac{3}{4}$

c. performed by a small group

d. set of beats

e. $\mathbf{C}$

f. weak beat before the downbeat

g. music that has two or more meters

h. a song from Cuba

i. $\frac{5}{8}$

j. played by the Dave Brubeck Quartet

k. strong beat at the beginning of a measure

l. tells which kind of note gets one beat

m. tells how many beats in a measure

Name _____ Date _____

Map of Native American Nations

Look at this historic map of Native American nations. You will need red, yellow, green, and blue markers, crayons, pens, or pencils. Color the map according to the directions below.

1. The Alligator Dance is usually performed by the Mohawk nation, but it probably originated among which tribes? Color the areas for these tribes red.

2. "Jó Ashílá" is a Navajo song that is part of a Squaw Dance presented to ward away violence and the effects of war. Color the area for Navajo nation yellow.

3. Think about the state in which you live. Which Indian nation once lived there? _____ Color your state green.

4. The Iroquois Confederacy, which included the Mohawks, was located in which state? _____

Mohawk Alligator Dance

Tekanionton'néha' (Alligator Dance)
Many Native American dances have names that honor animals, such as the Eagle Dance, Bear Dance, Rabbit Dance, and Alligator Dance. Native Americans also revere the circle symbol. It is often used in ceremonial and social dances. The Mohawk Alligator Dance explained below is one example of a circle dance.

Formation: In a double circle, partners stand side by side, facing counterclockwise. Girls form the outside ring, with boys on the inside ring. Each girl holds her partner's right elbow with her left hand; the boy's right arm is slightly bent in an escorting position.

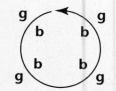

Basic Step: Drums and rattles set the tempo. When singing begins, the dancers move forward in a counterclockwise circle. They use a simple left/right shuffle. Feet are lifted slightly, not dragged. Dancers take two steps per beat, keeping a left-right-left-right eighth-note rhythm.

Turn: Each time the singers perform a whole note, all of the dancers execute a four-beat turn. The boy does the basic step in place while turning 360 degrees counterclockwise. Meanwhile, the girl, holding her partner's elbow, dances around her partner in a 360-degree counterclockwise circle. After completing the turn, the dancers resume the basic step.

Each time the song reaches the third line, the dancers (group) respond to the lead singer (solo) as shown in the music notation. The lead singer sings *yo ho* and the dancers and other singers answer *wi ye*.

Navajo Dance: "Jó Ashílá"

The Navajo of the Southwest call their song and dance ceremonies "ways." These ceremonies are similar to plays, but they can last for several days and include sand painting and chanting.

"Jó Ashílá" is part of a Navajo ceremony designed to protect the nation from violence and war. Native Americans believe that songs are gifts from the creator. They also greatly value their dances.

Movement for "Jó Ashílá" (Traveling Together)

Formation: In a double circle, partners stand side by side, facing clockwise. Boys are on the outside, forming the outer circle, and girls are on the inside, forming an inner circle. Each girl holds her partner's right elbow with her left hand. The boy's right arm is slightly bent in an escorting position. The drummer is in the center of the circle.

Basic Step: Dancers perform the Navajo Two-step with this song. A dancer may start on either foot. Dancers should move with a slight bounce to each step and travel in a clockwise circle.

Optional: At the end of the dance, the boy gives the girl a small gift. This might be a coin or an object such as a scarf.

Labeling Percussion Instruments

RESOURCE MASTER 6•11

In learning about tone color, you will learn to hear the differences among percussion instruments.

Label each instrument pictured below with its correct name.

bass drum	timpani	castanets	snare drum	xylophone	triangle
woodblock	tambourine	cymbals	maracas	gong	tom-tom

1. _____   2. _____   3. _____

4. _____   5. _____   6. _____

7. _____   8. _____   9. _____

10. _____ 11. _____ 12. _____

Name _____ Date _____

Evaluating Singers

When you evaluate someone's singing at a live performance, you can think about their performance in the following six general categories. Next time you attend a live performance (or watch a performance on television or at the movies), complete the following evaluation form by circling the number on the scale that accurately represents the performance in each category. Add the numbers to see what overall score you would give the singer.

5 – Excellent; very little room for improvement
4 – Very good; work on just a few details in this area is needed
3 – Average; needs to concentrate on improving in this area
4 – Below average; needs a lot of work in this area
5 – Unacceptable; the poor performance in this area distracts from the overall success of the performance

Energy, breath, and projection   **5 4 3 2 1**

Articulation and diction   **5 4 3 2 1**

Pitch accuracy   **5 4 3 2 1**

Posture and movement   **5 4 3 2 1**

Tone quality   **5 4 3 2 1**

Correct rhythm   **5 4 3 2 1**

Total score for singer: _____
(Divide this number by 6 to get an average across all six categories.)

Average score for singer: _____

Name _____ Date _____

Writing a Poem About Music

Compose your own poem about the importance of music in your world. Think about these questions.

What message do you want to share with the world? _____

_____

_____

What images can show your message? _____

_____

_____

_____

What rhyme scheme will you use? _____

_____

_____

What music metaphors can you include? (For example, you might use the term *harmony* as a metaphor for world peace.) _____

_____

_____

_____

After you write, remember to edit and revise your poem.
Make each word count!

Spotlight Your Success! RESOURCE MASTER 6•14

Review. Circle the correct answer.

1. Which beat grouping will work for $\frac{7}{8}$ meter?

   a. 3 + 2 + 2   **b.** 4 + 2 + 3   **c.** 3 + 2

2. Which diagram shows the conducting pattern for $\frac{3}{4}$?

   a. 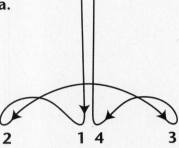   **b.**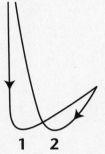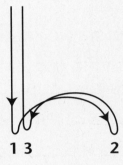

3. What is the name of a famous jazz piece in $\frac{5}{4}$ meter?

   a. "Give Me Five"   **b.** "Five by Four"   **c.** "Take Five"

4. What language is used in "El vito"?

   a. Spanish   **b.** Bulgarian   **c.** Navajo

Read and Listen. Circle the correct answer.

1. **Read** this meter. Then listen. Which meter do you hear?

   a. changing meter   **b.** $\frac{3}{4}$ **c.** $\frac{5}{8}$

2. **Read** this meter. Then listen. Which meter do you hear?

   a. changing meter   **b.** $\frac{4}{4}$ **c.** $\frac{7}{8}$

Spotlight Your Success! RESOURCE MASTER

3. **Read** this meter. Then listen. What meter do you hear?

a. $\frac{2}{4}$ b. $\frac{5}{8}$ c. $\frac{7}{8}$

Think! Write your answers.

1. What effect do you think good singing posture would have on an audience? Why? _____

   _____

2. If you were a composer, how would you determine what meter to write a song in? _____

   _____

3. Compare the characteristics of traditional Native American music with those of a favorite song. _____

   _____

4. **Write** why you think irregular meters are not common in American music. _____

   _____

Create and Perform

1. **Choose** a beat grouping for $\frac{7}{8}$.

2. **Write** a four-measure rhythm.

$\frac{7}{8}$ |＿＿＿＿＿＿＿|＿＿＿＿＿＿＿|＿＿＿＿＿＿＿‖

3. **Play** your rhythm on a pitched or unpitched instrument.

Name _____ Date _____

Self-Assessment

Who worked with you on the unit project? Write everyone's name. Tell the best thing that each person contributed to the project.

_____

_____

_____

What did you like best about the project? _____

_____

What did you like least? _____

_____

How helpful was the checklist on Resource Master 6-3? Did you use it with each song? Did it help you focus as you practiced?

_____

_____

If you could do the project again, what would you change—either about the project itself or about your work on it? _____

_____

How did your group do during the performance?
Use the checklist on Resource Master 6-3 one more time. This time, evaluate the whole performance instead of just one song.

Teacher Assessment

RESOURCE MASTER

	Blend of Voices	Expression	Stage Presence
Excellent	Voices blended together homogeneously, and the sound was very pleasing throughout the performance.	Vocal and facial expression interpreted and enhanced the meaning of the songs.	Performed with a great deal of energy, focus, and confidence.
*Competent	Voices blended together well, and the sound was pleasing throughout almost all of the performance.	Vocal and facial expression conveyed the meaning of the songs.	Performed with noticeable energy, focus, and confidence.
Progressing	Voices generally blended together, but occasionally a few individual voices could be heard.	Vocal and facial expression gave a sense of the meaning of the songs.	Performed with some energy, focus, and confidence.
Showing Little Progress	Individual voices were often heard that did not blend with the ensemble sound.	Vocal and facial expression did not seem to relate to the meaning of the original song.	Performed with little energy, focus, and/or confidence.

Not Scorable: Did not participate.

*Competent is the expected level for all students.

Pitches in Two Keys

RESOURCE MASTER R•1

Imitate four-beat ascending and descending patterns of *do, re, mi* by singing and using hand signs.

Read the melody shown below.

1. Say the rhythm.

2. Clap the rhythm.

3. Sing the pitches, using pitch syllables and hand signs.

4. Write the pitch syllables under each note.

Write the above exercise in the key of D major. Observe that when *do* and *mi* are on spaces, *re* is on the line between them.

Melodies with Do, Re, Mi

- Practice saying these words of wisdom with the class.

- Choose one of the rhythms, and play it on an unpitched instrument.

- Create a new melody by singing or playing your chosen rhythm and using *do re mi,* with G as *do.* Four melodies can be an interlude between repetitions of the song "Words of Wisdom" found on page 244 of your textbook.

When you've fin-ished chang-ing, you're fin-ished!

He that falls in love with him-self will have no ri-vals.

Lit-tle strokes fell great oaks.

Drive your bus'-ness or it will drive thee!

Musical Concentration

Work in pairs, with each partner cutting out a complete set of cards. Combine all cards, and place them facedown. Take turns turning over two cards at a time. When a matching pair is found, the other person is to sing those notes. If the notes are sung accurately, that person takes the pair. Use a pitched instrument to check for pitch accuracy. If the notes are not sung accurately, the first person gets the cards. If the cards do not match, turn them facedown again. The winner is the person with the most pairs when all matches have been made.

At the end of the game, arrange several cards to compose original melodies. Play the melodies on a pitched instrument.

Musical Concentration

mi re do
A G F

mi do mi
A F A

mi mi re
A A G

mi do re
A F G

la mi la mi
D A D A

so mi re do
C A G F

so mi do re
C A F G

so do so do
C F C F

so la so la
C D C D

so la so mi
C D C A

Musical Concentration

so la mi do
C D A F

so la so do
C D C F

do so la so
F C D C

mi do mi do
A F A F

la so la so
D C D C

la so mi so
D C A C

mi re mi re
A G A G

mi so mi so
A C A C

mi la so mi
A D C A

so mi
C A

Composing with *Do, Re, Mi*

Using Haydn's idea of starting each phrase with *do, re, mi,* you can compose a melody. Use his idea again, and end with *do, re, mi* as well. These *do, re, mi* pitches are filled in for you on the staves at the bottom of the page. Write the rest of the melody, using any pitches in the F pentatonic scale.

Make sure that you have notes or rests that add up to two beats in each measure. Use only quarter notes, eighth-note pairs, and quarter rests for this melody.

Remember:

♩ = one beat   𝄽 = one beat   ♫ = one beat

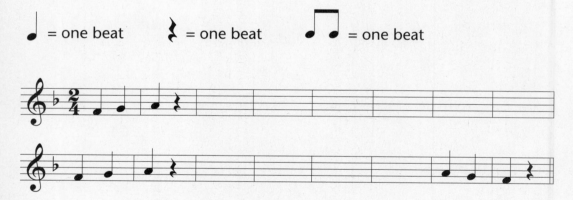

Syncopation

Syncopation occurs when the accent beat of a note falls on the off-beat, or unaccented beat. It provides an interesting rhythm. Syncopation is often used in jazz music, which has its roots in African music.

Here is an example of some measures without syncopation. Clap the beats.

Here are some similar measures that have syncopation. Clap the beats.

Now have someone clap a steady 4-beat tempo and clap the syncopated pattern with them. Do you hear how the syncopated beats sometimes fall between the beats of the steady tempo?

Here is a call-and-response song called "The African Plain." Have half the class sing the call. Then have the other half of the class sing the response. Finally, have both groups sing together.

Circle the notes that are syncopated in "The African Plain."

The African Plain

Lyrics and Music
© 2004 Coleen Hitchcock

Call
Ah le um um ah le um um

Response
Da da da dum dum dum da da da dum dum dum

Call
Ah le um um ah le um um

Response
Da da da dum dum dum da da da dum dum dum

Dotted Quarters and Eighths

Practice writing the syncopated pattern by copying it in the empty boxes below.

Practice writing the  pattern by copying it in the empty boxes below.

Clap the following rhythm patterns:

a.    c.

b.    d.

Write the pattern that you hear your teacher play.

1. _____

2. _____

3. _____

4. _____

Name _____ Date _____

Writing Syncopation

RESOURCE MASTER

Clap these rhythms:

To create a four-measure percussion composition, arrange the rhythms in the four blank measures below in any order you like . You may use all four patterns or repeat one of them. End with a rest in the last measure so that the composition sounds complete.

Practice playing your rhythm on a percussion instrument of your choice.

For a challenge, play your composition at the same time that a partner plays his or her composition on a contrasting-sounding percussion instrument.

Improvising on Themes

Here is the rhythm pattern Beethoven used in the overture to the play *King Stephen:*

Syncopated Theme

Improvise a melody for this pattern on these pitches:

The arrows beneath the bars above show pitches that you can play for a falling fourth introduction, like Beethoven's. These pitches are in a different key than the one Beethoven used so that they can be played on instruments set up for the C pentatonic scale.

Play the falling fourth motive as an introduction for your improvisations.

Use the staff below to write a composed melody in C pentatonic, using Beethoven's rhythm.

Melodies with *Fa*

Fill in the missing pitch syllables, sing them, and then write the title of the song on the line below. Remember that if *mi* and *so* are on lines, *fa* is in the space between those two lines.

do __ __ do do __ __ do mi __ so mi __ so

Title: _____

Write this melody in C major. Play it on a pitched instrument.

do re mi fa so so so so fa mi re do do do

Play the melody, using F as *do*. Then write it below in the key of F. What key signature will you need to add?

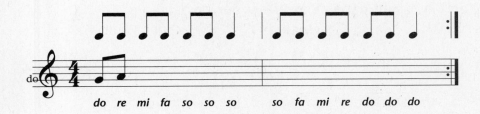

do re mi fa so so so so fa mi re do do do

Composing with *Fa*

RESOURCE MASTER

You can compose a melody, using some ideas from *Song of Peace* on page 257 of your textbook. Look at the song to notice several things about the melody.

1. *Fa* is always approached and left by only a step or a skip.

2. Only the last phrase ends on *do.*

3. Each phrase ends on a long note.

Compose your own melody, using the above ideas. Use *fa* at least once. Use only these pitches:

Use $\frac{4}{4}$ rhythm. Make sure that you have notes or rests that add up to four beats in each measure.

Remember: 𝅝 = four beats 𝅗𝅥 = two beats 𝅘𝅥. = $1\frac{1}{2}$ beats 𝅘𝅥 = one beat

𝄽 = one beat 𝅘𝅥𝅘𝅥 = one beat 𝅘𝅥𝅮 = $\frac{1}{2}$ beat

Write your melody on blank staff paper. Play it for your class.

A Melody with Fa and Ti

Compose a melody, using both *fa* and *ti.* Use both *fa* and *ti* at least once. Use only these pitches:

Move to and from *fa* and *ti* by step for the smoothest-sounding melody. In other words, keep the interval of a second before and after each *fa* and *ti.*

Use the staff below to write your melody. Begin each line of your melody on C (*do*). End the melody on *do* as well.

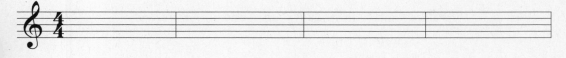

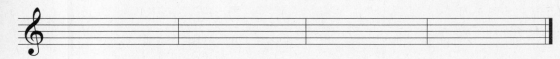

Check the rhythm! Make sure that you have notes or rests that add up to three beats in each measure.

Remember: $\bar{}$ = three beats $\bar{}$ = two beats $\bar{}$ = $1\frac{1}{2}$ beats $\bar{}$ = one beat

$\bar{}$ = one beat $\bar{}$ = one beat $\bar{}$ = $\frac{1}{2}$ beat

Play both lines twice to give the melody ABAB form.

Singing in $\frac{3}{4}$ Meter

RESOURCE MASTER

"The Streets of Laredo" is a well-known cowboy song.

1. Sing the song.

Streets of Laredo

Cowboy Song

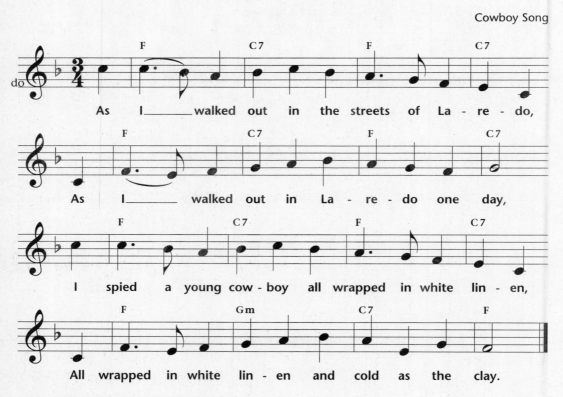

2. Circle the *fa* in the song.

3. Circle the *ti* in the song.

Sixteenth Notes

Use this chart as a reference for various rhythms.

Compare the notes in both columns. The beamed notes on the left are equal to the tied notes on the right.

Write eight measures of rhythm, using sixteenth-note rhythms as well as other rhythms. Use ♫, ♬, and ♪.♪, at least once in your composition.

Play the measures on unpitched percussion instruments.

$\frac{2}{4}$

Sixteenth Combinations

Complete the measures below so that there are two beats in every measure. Empty beats are indicated with a line _____. Use each of these rhythms at least once.

♫♫ = four sixteenths = 1 beat divided into four equal parts

♪.♬ = dotted eighth and sixteenth = 1 beat divided into four equal parts with the first three parts tied together

♬♪ = two sixteenths and an eighth = 1 beat divided into four equal parts with the last two parts tied together

Play your eight-measure pattern on a percussion instrument during the verse or refrain of "Cindy," found in page 265 of your textbook.

Now that you have your rhythm pattern, here are some other things to do with it.

1. Play your rhythm pattern as a partner conducts.

2. Play the rhythm pattern at different tempos.

3. Perform your pattern at the same time that a partner performs his or her rhythm pattern.

4. Write words for the rhythm pattern, and then speak them.

Name _____ Date _____

Composing an Ostinato

Create an ostinato for "Los Maizales" found on page 268 of your textbook.

Here are some guidelines:

1. Make the pattern four beats (two measures) long, using any of these rhythms:

$\half$ = two beats $\dottedquarter$ = $1\frac{1}{2}$ beats $\quarter$ = one beat $\restquarter$ = one beat

$\beamedeighths$ one = beat $\eighth$ = $\frac{1}{2}$ beat $\triplet$ one = beat $\tripletrest$ one = beat

2. Use syncopated pattern—  —one time.

3. For rhythmic variety with the melody, do not use the same rhythm as the melody at any point. Make the pattern easy enough to do repeatedly without confusion or physical stress. Keep it less important than the melody. The ostinato is an accompaniment!

4. Check the rhythm! Make sure that you have notes or rests that add up to two beats in each measure.

Write one possibility below. Play it with the song on a percussion instrument of your choice. Make any changes you wish.

$\frac{2}{4}$ ‖: | :‖

Share your final version with the class, singing the song.

Minor Pitches

Below are the pitches for a song called "On Planning Family Vacations," which expresses a problem that one person has. As you will soon discover, the melody is that of "By the Singing Water" (page 270 of your textbook)— backwards!

Sing this song with the words. Not all songs make a good tune when sung backwards. Sing this one, and see what you think.

On Planning Family Vacations
("By the Singing Water" - backwards)

Adapted and Words by
Marilyn C. Davidson

Write the pitch syllable names under each note in the spaces provided.

"River" Melody

Create your own eight-measure melody in D minor, in $\frac{6}{8}$ meter. If you like, dedicate it to a river of your choice!

Put your title here: _____

Use step-wise motion for your melody, as Smetana did, to help the melody suggest a flowing river. Use Smetana's rhythm or your own. Use any of these pitches:

Write your melody on this staff.

Play or sing your minor melody.

A Major Change!

Now, change your melody to D major by changing any F natural to F#, any C natural to C#, and any B flat to B natural. You should then have only the following pitches:

Play or sing your melody now. See whether you notice the difference in the musical effect when the melody is major instead of minor.

Building Chords

Complete the chords. Name the pitches needed, and write in both the pitch syllables and letter names.

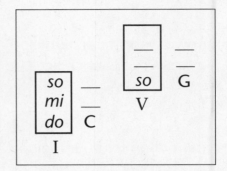

Draw the notes for the chords on the staff. Notes for chords are written directly above one another.

Complete the notation below to create a new musical phrase. For the melody, use any pitches of the I chord (C E G) or of the V chord (G B D). Use the set of pitches that goes with the chord's names in the harmony part. Fill in the chord pitches to complete the harmony part. Work with a partner. Play your music on bells.

Learning About Rests RESOURCE MASTER

Shown below is the Hawaiian folk song "Nani Wale Na Hala," which means "beautiful pandanus trees swaying by the sea."

Nani Wale Na Hala

Hawaiian Folk Song

Circle the eighth rests in this song.

Working in groups, form three musical tribes: the Dolphins, the Whales, and the Sharks. Have each group practice making these three sounds.

1. Click your tongue to make the sound of the dolphins.

2. Hum to make the sound of the whale (say "Omm").

3. For the shark, say "Got you!"

When you play the song, have the Whale group hum where the first rest is located in the song. The Dolphin group will click on the second rest. At the end of the song, the Shark group will say, "Got you."

A Blues Bass Line

RESOURCE MASTER

Play this blues bass line with "City Blues" found on page 278 of your textbook.

Practice the bass line on this keyboard. Then take turns playing it on any pitched instrument. Use a low-sounding instrument if possible.

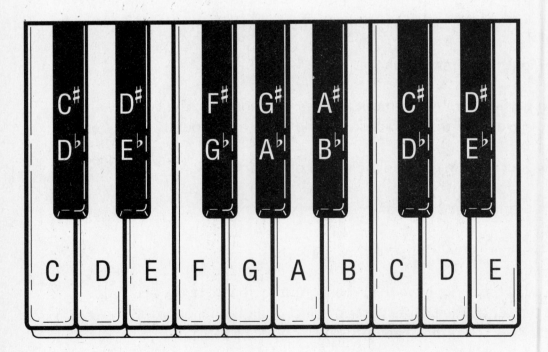

Using I-IV-V Chords

RESOURCE MASTER

Write the letters of the chord roots. This song is in G major.

Song text follows:

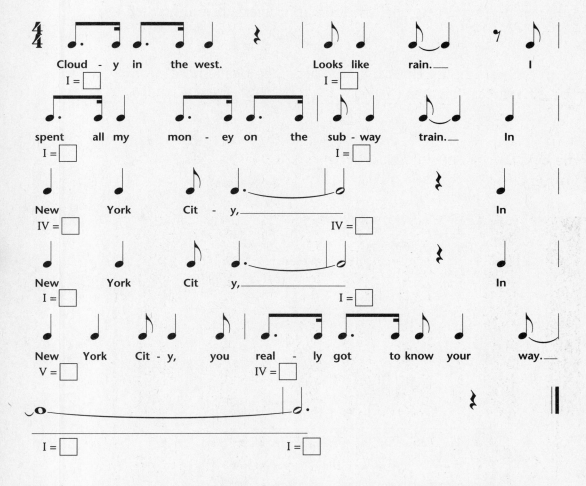

Sing the chord roots with the song. Play the chords on autoharps or other chording instruments.

Composing Music in $\frac{5}{4}$ Meter

An accent is a stress on a note or chord. In $\frac{5}{4}$ meter, the accents are usually on beats one and three or beats one and four. This gives a grouping of 2 + 3 or 3 + 2.

Read and clap each example below. Clap the accented beats more strongly. Describe the differences between them.

Come Home

Words and Music by
Colleen Hitchcock

Pond Frog

Words and Music by
Colleen Hitchcock

Name _____ Date _____

Changing Meters

In the late nineteenth century, an entertainer named Pat Rooney delighted audiences with the song "Is That Mr. Reilly?"

1. Identify the meter of the song, and then sing the song.

Is That Mister Reilly?

Words and Music by Pat Rooney

Is that Mis-ter Reil-ly, can an-y-one tell?

Is that Mis-ter Reil-ly that owns the ho-tel?

Well, if that's Mis-ter Reil-ly, they speak of you high-ly.

Well up-on my soul Reil-ly, you're do-ing quite well.

Charles Ives was an American composer who enjoyed using rhythm and meters to treat well-known melodies in unique and sometimes amusing ways. He used the melody of "Is That Mr. Reilly?" and changed the meter to create the song "The Side Show" found on page 203 of your textbook.

2. Listen to "The Side Show," and count the beats.

3. Listen to "The Side Show," and clap the rhythm.

4. Create your own lyrics and version of "Is That Mr. Reilly?" and perform your version.

Name _____ Date _____

Composing Rhythms

Practice saying these patterns in $\frac{5}{4}$. Then identify the patterns that your teacher claps.

Choose one pattern, and write it here.

Play your pattern on a hand drum with "Leggiero" from Music for Children on page 281.

Practice saying these patterns in $\frac{7}{8}$. Then identify the patterns that your teacher claps.

Choose one pattern, and write it here.

Play your pattern on tambourine with "Samiotissa."

Name _____ Date _____

Singing in $\frac{3}{2}$ Meter

The three most important parts of a song are the melody, the lyrics, and the rhythm. An exciting rhythm can make us remember the song and want to dance whenever we hear it. Pay attention to the rhythm in this song, and note how the rhythm and melody together make it easy to remember the song, even after hearing it only once.

1. Pat the rhythm in $\frac{3}{4}$ meter to the first two measures of "In a Hurry."

2. Pat the rhythm in $\frac{3}{2}$ meter to the second two measures of "In a Hurry."

3. What kind of note gets one beat in the rhythm pattern?

4. What is the difference between the notes in measures one, two, five, and six of the song? In measures three, four, seven, and eight of the song? How are these notes the same?

In a Hurry

Words and Music by
Colleen Hitchcock

I am in a hur-ry   And I am   slow-ing down.

When I have to scu-ry,   It's hard to   get a-round.

Beat Bars

——— ——— ——— ———

——— ——— ——— ———

——— ——— ——— ———

——— ——— ——— ———

Pitch Ladder

RESOURCE MASTER R•27

Curwen Hand Signs

RESOURCE MASTER R•28

do

ti

la

so

fa

mi

re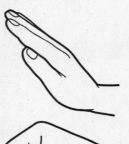

do

Name _____ Date _____

Scale Stairs

Note Values

The Music Man Junior

RESOURCE MASTER **P•1**

Book, Music, and Lyrics by Meredith Willson
Story by Meredith Willson and Franklin Lacey

CAST		
Charlie Cowell	Harold Hill	Mrs. Paroo
Salesmen	Marcellus	Winthrop
Conductor	Mayor Shinn	

Scene 1: A Train on the Way to River City, Iowa

Song 1: Rock Island

SALESMAN 1
Tch, tch, tch, tch

SALESMAN 2
Ever meet a fella by the name a' Hill?

SALESMAN 1
Hill?

CHARLIE
Hill!

SALESMAN 3
Hill?

SALESMAN 4
Hill?

NEWSPAPER READER 1
Hill?

NEWSPAPER READER 2
Hill?

ALL BUT CHARLIE
No!

SALESMAN 2
Now he doesn't know the territory.

SALESMAN 1
Doesn't know the territory?

SALESMAN 4
Look, whad-a-ya talk, whad-a-ya talk, whad-a-ya talk,

SALESMAN 2
He's a Music Man and he sells clarinets to the kids in town,
with the big trombones and the rat-a-tat drums, and the big brass bass, big
brass bass . . .

SALESMAN 1
Well! I don't know much about bands,
but I do know you can't make a livin'
sellin' big trombones. No sir!

SALESMAN 2
No, the fella sells bands.
Boys' bands.
I don't know how he does it,
but he lives like a king,
and when the man dances, certainly boys,
What else: The piper pays him.

ALL
Yesss sir, yesss sir, yesss sir, yesss sir.

CHARLIE
But he doesn't know the territory!

End of Song

CONDUCTOR: River City, Iowa!

STRANGER (HAROLD HILL): Gentlemen, you intrigue me. I think I'll have to give Iowa a try.

CHARLIE COWELL: Don't believe I caught your name.

HAROLD: Don't believe I dropped it.

(HAROLD turns his suitcase towards the audience, which says "PROF. HAROLD HILL," and EXITS the train.)

SALESMAN 1: So, Harold Hill ventured into the small town of River City, Iowa, to try his luck.

Scene 2: The Main Street of River City, Iowa

Song 2: Iowa Stubborn (Company)

TOWNSPEOPLE
Oh, there's nothin' halfway
about the Iowa way to treat you,
when we treat you, which we may not do at all.

There's an Iowa kinda special
chip-on-the-shoulder attitude we've
never been without that we recall.

We can be cold as our falling thermometers
in December if you ask about our weather in July.
And we're so by gad stubborn,
we can stand touchin' noses for
a week at a time and never see eye-to-eye.

But what the heck! You're welcome,
join us at the picnic.
You can have your fill of all the food
you bring yourself.

You really ought to give Iowa
Hawkeye, Iowa, Dubuque, Des Moines, Davenport, Marshalltown,
Mason City, Keokuk, Ames, Clear Lake,
ought to give Iowa a try.

End of Song

(As the TOWNSPEOPLE go about their business, MARCELLUS spies HAROLD.)

SALESMAN 2: Harold Hill was surprised to run into his old buddy Marcellus Washburn.

MARCELLUS: What are you doing here? *(HAROLD pantomimes conducting.)* You're not back in the band business!

HAROLD: Yup!

MARCELLUS: But you don't know anything about music.

HAROLD: Marcellus, stop worrying.

MARCELLUS: We got a lady music teacher here who'll expose you before you get your bags unpacked.

HAROLD: If she passes by, point her out to me.

MARCELLUS: I will.

(HAROLD puts down his suitcase, and speaks loudly to MARCELLUS, drawing a crowd.)

Song 3: 76 Trombones

HAROLD
May I have your attention, please?
Attention, please!
I can deal with this trouble, friends,
with a wave of my hand, this very hand!

Please observe me if you will.
I'm Professor Harold Hill,
and I'm here to organize
the River City Boys' Band! Prrrrr!

Oh, a band'll do it, my friends, oh, yes!
I mean a boys' band, do you hear me?
I say River City's gotta have a boys' band,
and I mean she needs it today.

Well, Professor Harold Hill's on hand
and River City's gonna have her boys' band!
And that band's gonna be in uniform!

TOWNSPEOPLE
Seventy six trombones led the big parade,
with a hundred and ten cornets close at hand.
They were followed by rows and rows of the finest virtuosos,
the cream of ev'ry famous band.

Seventy six trombones caught the morning sun,
with a hundred and ten cornets right behind.
There were more than a thousand reeds springing up like weeds.
There were horns of ev'ry shape and kind.

There were fifty mounted cannon in the battery,
thundering, thundering, louder than before.
clarinets of evr'y size and
trumpeters who'd improvise
a full octave higher than the score.

Seventy six trombones hit the counterpoint,
while a hundred and ten cornets blazed away.
To the rhythm of Harch! Harch! Harch!
All the kids began to march,
and they're marching still right today!
Marching still right today!

End of Song

(There is a commotion of excitement from the TOWNSPEOPLE as most of them EXIT. MAYOR SHINN steps forward to talk to EWART, OLIN, OLIVER, and JACY of the School Board.)

SALESMAN 3: The mayor wasn't buying Harold Hill's remedy for the town's troubles.

SHINN: Gentlemen of the School Board, this calls for emergency action. That man is a spellbinder. Find out if he ever got his college music degree!

(SHINN EXITS. The SCHOOL BOARD approaches HAROLD as a few LADIES stay to listen in.)

SALESMAN 4: Harold Hill evaded the School Board's request for his degree by teaching them the joy of singing in harmony.

SALESMAN 5: Some of the ladies were suspicious too.

THE LADIES
(SING TWICE; THEN SING PART ON PAGE 148.)
Pick a little, talk a little,
Pick a little, talk a little,
Cheep, cheep, cheep,
Talk a lot, pick a little more.

Pick a little, talk a little,
Pick a little, talk a little,
Cheep, cheep, cheep,
Talk a lot, pick a little more.

Pick a little, talk a little,
Pick a little, talk a little,
Cheep, cheep, cheep,
Talk a lot, pick a little more.

Pick a little, talk a little,
Pick a little, talk a little,
Cheep, cheep, cheep, cheep,
Cheep, cheep, cheep, cheep!

SCHOOL BOARD
(SING TWICE WITH LADIES)
Goodnight, ladies, Goodnight, ladies,
Goodnight, ladies, we're going to leave you now.

Farewell, ladies, farewell, ladies,
farewell, ladies, we're going to leave you now.

THE LADIES
Pick a little, talk a little,
Pick a little, talk a little,
Pick a little, talk a little,
Pick a little, talk a little,
Cheep, cheep, cheep, cheep,
Cheep, cheep, cheep, cheep,

Cheep, cheep, cheep, cheep,
Cheep, cheep, cheep, cheep,

Cheep, cheep, cheep, cheep,
Cheep, cheep, cheep, cheep,
Pick a little, talk a little, cheep!

End of Song

Scene 3: Town Square

SALESMAN 5: Harold Hill continued to sell instruments to all the boys in town.

SALESMAN 1: And he kept escaping the School Board's requests for his credentials.

SALESMAN 2: Marian, the music teacher, was suspicious of Harold Hill, too.

MRS. PAROO: Marian, now what are you up to?

MARIAN: I have a feeling the *Indiana Journal* may help me poke some holes in the Professor's claims.

SALESMAN 3: Marian found some interesting information about Harold Hill's background at the library.

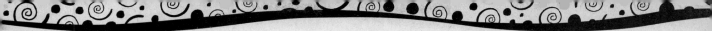

SALESMAN 4: He couldn't have graduated from college in Gary, Indiana, in aught 5 . . .

SALESMAN 5: . . . because the town wasn't even built until aught 6.

SALESMAN 1: Before Marian could take her evidence to the Mayor for inspection, an amazing thing happened.

MRS. PAROO: The Wells Fargo wagon is just comin' up from the depot!

SHINN: At this hour of the day?

WINTHROP: It could be the band instruments!

SHINN: The band instruments! I want that man's credentials!

(The whole town is excited and comes on to welcome the arrival of the Wells Fargo wagon.)

Song 5: The Wells Fargo Wagon (Company)

TOWNSPEOPLE
Oho, the Wells Fargo Wagon is a comin' down the street.
Oh, please, let it be for me.

Oho, the Wells Fargo Wagon is a comin' down the street.
I wish, I wish I knew what it could be.

1ST VOICE
I got a box of maple sugar on my birthday.

2ND VOICE
In March, I got a grey mackinaw.

3RD VOICE
And once, I got some grapefruit from Tampa . . .

4TH VOICE
Montgom'ry Ward sent me a bathtub and a crosscut saw.

TOWNSPEOPLE
Oho, the Wells Fargo Wagon is a comin' now.
Is it a prepaid surprise or C.O.D.?

5TH VOICE
It could be curtains, or dishes, or a double boiler.

6TH VOICE
Or it could be,

TOWNSPEOPLE
Yes, it could be,
Yes, you're right, it surely could be,

6TH VOICE
Somethin' special,

TOWNSPEOPLE
Somethin' very very special now,

6TH VOICE
just for me.

TOWNSPEOPLE
Oho, you Wells Fargo Wagon keep a comin',
Oho, you Wells Fargo Wagon keep a comin,
Oho, you Wells Fargo Wagon, don't you dare to make a stop,
until you stop for me.

End of Song

(MARIAN pushes her way through the CROWD to crush WINTHROP in an embrace.)

TOWNSPEOPLE: Hurray!

HAROLD: *(Handing WINTHROP the cornet.)* Here you are, Winthrop.

WINTHROP: My cornet! Gee thanks, Professor!

SHINN: Round one for you, Mister Hill, but I better hear some tootin' out'a them horns in pretty short order.

SALESMAN 1: Marian could see how happy Winthrop was—and all because of Harold Hill's band.

SALESMAN 2: In fact, the spirits of every person in town had been lifted.

SALESMAN 3: Harold Hill might have come to River City to sell people something they didn't need . . .

SALESMAN 4: . . . but what he gave them was something that changed their lives: The inspiring gift of music.

(COMPANY sings last verse of "76 Trombones" on page 146.)

Chusok

Chusok is like Thanksgiving in many ways. Both are harvest festivals. For both, families gather to eat special foods. And for both, people travel long distances to see their families.

In Korea, the special food for Chusok is *song pyon,* "half-moon cakes." Song pyon are dough stuffed with red or black beans, chestnuts, or other delicious fillings.

When you smell turkey roasting in the oven on Thanksgiving, you know that the meal will soon be on the table. In Korea, dinner is ready when the house smells like pine. That's because the song pyon rest on a bed of pine needles while they cook. When the song pyon are done, the pine needles are washed off. Then the song pyon are rubbed with sesame oil. Finally, they're ready to eat.

More people travel during Chusok than at any other time of the year. A normal three- or four-hour trip from the city of Seoul to the countryside might take as long as 15 to 20 hours because of the crowds!

People travel so many hours because visiting family is very important. During Chusok, families visit the graves of their ancestors. They spend part of the holiday pulling weeds and planting flowers at the gravesites.

Here is a song that is often performed on the night before Chusok. Chant the words to get the feeling of the song.

*In the heavens there are
   many stars.
Kang Kang Sue Wol Lae.
Friends are great, gardens are beautiful.
Kang Kang Sue Wol Lae.*

*There are many pine trees,
   there are many pine needles.
Kang Kang Sue Wol Lae.
There are many bamboo trees.
Kang Kang Sue Wol Lae.*

Fill in the chart with the correct answers about Chusok.

Special Food	
Special Smell	
Special Activity	

Diwali

To celebrate Diwali, people let their artistic talents go wild. Creating sweet treats, making gifts for family and friends, writing and then staging your own plays, and composing your own songs and dances are some ways to show off your talents. Diwali is also a time to forgive old enemies, ask for their forgiveness in turn, and make an effort to be closer to family and friends.

Let your artistic side shine by writing your own song. Try composing lyrics to fit a piece of music you've listened to during your study of Diwali. Choose one of these ideas, or use them to inspire your own lyrics.

- Diwali is a festival during which the talents of young people are often discovered. Write lyrics about what you want to do when you grow up.

- Have your lyrics tell about a favorite family activity, such as playing a board game, eating your evening meal together, or going on vacation.

- Use the lyrics to tell a friend that you forgive him or her for _____. Or, ask a friend to forgive you for _____.

- Write lyrics that describe how you felt toward a sibling or parent when you participated in a particular event, such as a wedding or holiday celebration, with your extended family.

Halloween Puzzle

RESOURCE MASTER $\quad$ C•3

Read the clues, and fill the blanks with your answers.

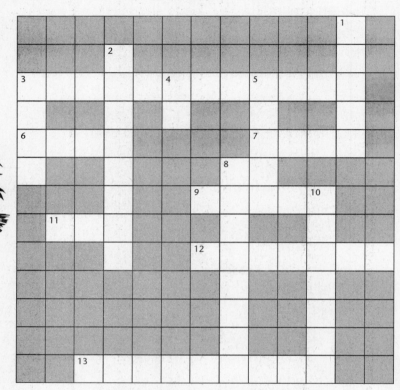

Across

3 It probably grew up in a patch

6 Enthusiasm

7 Not hard

8 Pa is married to her

9 She rides a broomstick

11 How a ghost might greet you

12 What you wear on Halloween

13 A spooky place to visit, especially on Halloween

Down

1 What you most often get when you go trick or treating

2 Its bones are dry

3 The kind of music for which Duke Ellington is famous

4 The sixth tone in the diatonic scale

5 Not a trick, but a _____

8 Spooky Halloween music might be written in a _____ (2 words)

10 The kind of house in which a ghost lives

Name _____ Date _____

Winter Word Scramble

Here are some words that have to do with winter, but they're all mixed up! First, unscramble them. Then use as many of them as you can to write a winter song. Write your song to the tune of "Jingle Bells" or "Winter Wonderland." As you write, think about how your lyrics might change if you were to write your song to a different tune.

1 DOWBNAROS _____

2 KYCHOE _____

3 KESATS _____

4 LOWDANDERN _____

5 ECCILI _____

6 GOTONGAB _____

7 CEATJK _____

8 SWONESSOH _____

9 SMETINT _____

10 LZBIAZDR _____

Dreidel

Dreidel (or dreidl) is a Hanukkah game played with a four-sided top and tokens, such as candy pieces. In Hebrew, the letters on each side of the top stand for the phrase *Nes Gadol Hayah Sham*, which means "a great miracle happened here." In Yiddish, the letters stand for the game instructions.

Here's how to play. Each player gets an equal number of tokens. Each puts one token in the middle of the circle. Then players take turns spinning the dreidel. When the dreidel falls, the player who spun it does whatever the letter facing up instructs, as explained below. The game is over when one player has all the tokens.

Nun   *Nun* stands for *nisht*, which means "nothing" in Yiddish. Lose a turn.

Gimel *Gimel* stands for *gants*, which means "whole." Take the whole pot.

Hey   *Hey* stands for *halb*, which means "half." Take half.

Shin   *Shin* stands for *shetl*, which means "put in." Put in some number of tokens. Your group determines this number before the game starts.

Make some copies of the dreidel pattern on the other page of this lesson. Use a punch to make a hole in the top and bottom. Fold along the lines. Fold in the tabs, and glue them to the sides to make a box. Put a short, sharpened pencil through the holes. Form a group of three to six players, and start playing!

Dreidel Pattern

RESOURCE MASTER C•5

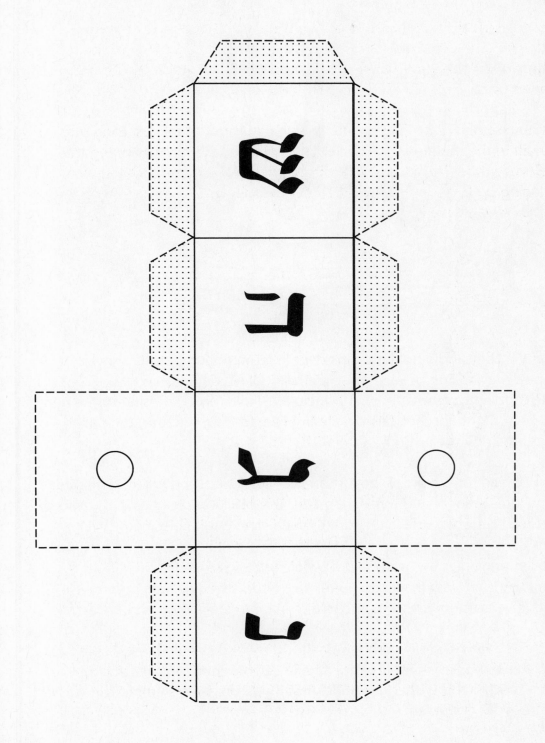

The Kinara

RESOURCE MASTER

The *kinara,* the candle holder, helps people remember Kwanzaa's seven principles *(Nguzo Saba)*. Each principle has its own day during Kwanzaa. The middle candle represents the first principle, *Umoja* (unity). It is lit on the first night. Each night another candle is lit in order (see the picture) until all the candles are lit by the last day.

The candles are the colors of the African flag: black, red, and green. One candle is black, three are red, and three are green. The black candle goes in the middle. The red candles go on the left, and the green candles go on the right.

The seven principles of Kwanzaa are *Umoja* (unity), *Kujichagulia* (self-determination), *Ujima* (collective work and responsibility), *Ujamaa* (cooperative economics), *Nia* (purpose), *Kuumba* (creativity), and *Imani* (faith).

Kwanzaa is a new holiday compared with others, so people are encouraged to apply *kuumba* (creativity) in their family celebrations. Perhaps you can create a song to remember the principles. If you do, keep in mind the vocal structures you've studied.

Make an Instrument RESOURCE MASTER C•7

People have always made music. If they couldn't buy instruments, they made their own. Ancient peoples made music by adding strings or gourds to their hunting bows to make different sounds. They stretched animal hides over wood and sewed on shells to make tambourines.

In old-time jug bands, someone blew across or into a jug to create a bass line. The jug was called the poor man's tuba. Other rhythm "instruments" in these old bands included washboards and washtubs.

After the Civil War, people used whatever they could find to make their instruments. "Real" instruments were too expensive or else were unavailable, even if you had the money.

With a classmate, make your own instrument. Use recycled materials to make a drum, chime, shaker, flute, or something of your own invention.

A simple tambourine is easy to make. Glue two heavy paper plates together. Punch holes around the edges, and tie on jingle bells.

Try something fancier, if you like! If the whole class brings in materials, you'll be amazed at what you can invent. Some good starting materials are metal, plastic, or heavy cardboard tubes; empty coffee cans; old guitar or violin strings; fishing line; wire hangers; wooden or metal spoons; old keys; discarded hubcaps; clay pots; plastic cups; and raw beans and rice. Use glue, nails, string, tape, or staples to hold your instrument together. When you're finished, name your instrument and play it!

Cinco de Mayo

RESOURCE MASTER C•8

Read below to find out why Cinco de Mayo is an important day of celebration.

In 1862, Mexico owed a great deal of money to the English, Spanish, and French. England, Spain, and France sent people to Mexico to find out how the money would be paid back. The English and Spanish worked out a solution with President Benito Juarez and left.

The French had other ideas. They wanted to rule Mexico. They had even brought along a noble; they planned to make him ruler of Mexico! However, President Juarez did not intend to let this happen. On May 5, he sent General Zaragosa to wait for the French in the little town of Puebla.

The French soldiers weren't worried. They had many men and were well-equipped for fighting. They thought that the Mexicans would just give up! The soldiers marched as though they had no cares at all.

It began raining and thundering. The march became rough. One story says that it was made even rougher by Indians who were helping the Mexicans. Armed only with machetes, these Indians stampeded hundreds of cattle into the middle of the French soldiers. The French finally attacked the town of Puebla, but the Mexicans fought fiercely and won the battle.

It took five more years of war, though, before the Mexicans could rid their country of the French. Still, the battle at Puebla gave them the courage to go on fighting. That is why Cinco de Mayo is celebrated today.

Fill in the chart with facts about the origins of Cinco de Mayo.

The country fighting against Mexico	
The Mexican town where the battle took place	
The date of the battle	

Now that you know the facts about Cinco de Mayo, think about how you might write music that represents each part of the story. Discuss with a partner or a group why some instruments might work better than others for certain parts of the story. Work in groups to compose a song.

Powwow Dances

RESOURCE MASTER   C•9

Dancing is an important part of the ceremonies during a Native American Powwow. People also dance for fun and compete for prizes during Powwows. There are many types of dances and many age groups.

Go to the library or media center and do research on "Powwow dances." Find pictures of the following dances and read about them. Then draw a line from the name of the dance to its description.

Name

1 Women's Jingle Dance
2 Women's Fancy Shawl Dance
3 Women's Northern Traditional Dance
4 Women's Southern Traditional Dance
5 Men's Grass Dance
6 Men's Fancy Dance
7 Men's Northern Traditional Dance
8 Men's Southern Straight Dance

Description

a The beat inspires complex footwork that creates a graceful whirl of controlled movement.

b Dancers dip and sway to the drumbeat, taking slow, bouncing steps.

c Dancers hang yarn or ribbon from their arms and waists. Their movements are graceful and flowing.

d Barely moving, dancers bend their knees slowly to the beat of the drum. The up-and-down motion is graceful.

e The traditional purpose of this dance is healing. The dance steps are complicated and slow.

f Outfits may be handed down from generation to generation. Onlookers stand and take off their hats to honor the eagle feathers in the costumes.

g Dancers wear buckskin pants and bone breastplates for this dance.

h This is the most athletic Powwow dance. Singers try to trick the dancers with surprise end beats.

Listening Map Instructions

LM-1 Blue Moon of Kentucky by Bill Monroe

Use with Unit 1, Lesson 5

Distribute a copy of the listening map to each student. Point out the various instruments in the key. Bluegrass music is usually played with different solo instruments taking the lead for part of a song. Ask students to identify the instruments as they hear them. Divide the students into two groups for a meter exercise. Have one group stamp feet on beat 1 and the other group clap the remaining beats for each tempo and meter. Students could learn to dance the waltz and two-step to the music.

Bill Monroe, who wrote "Blue Moon of Kentucky" is known as the "father of bluegrass." His band was one of the first to make this style of music popular. Monroe was known as a singer and mandolin player. He was a tenor, and he helped develop a particular style of bluegrass singing that became known as the "high lonesome sound."

LM-2 Ode to a Butterfly by Chris Thile

Use with Unit 1, Lesson 5

Distribute a copy of the listening map to each student. Point out the various instruments shown in the key. Ask students to identify the instruments as they hear them. Ask students to close their eyes and describe the character of each instrument and the images the sound of each instrument evokes.

Ask students to compare how these descriptions relate to the size and structure of these instruments. Have students describe what event or function this music might be used for.

LM-4 Maggie in the Wood (traditional Irish song)

Use with Unit 2, Lesson 1

Distribute a copy of the listening map to each student. Ask students to identify the instruments they hear. The placement of each instrument on the listening map indicates the entrance or prominence of that instrument at that time. Ask students to identify the difference in pitch and tone color between the penny whistle and Irish flute (penny whistle higher, thinner tone color); Irish flute (lower, warmer sound). What instrument do the bones sound like? (castanets) Explain that the Irish hand drum, the bodhran, is the other percussion instrument they hear.

LM-8 Symphony No. 9 in D minor, ("Choral"), Fourth Movement (excerpt) by Ludwig van Beethoven

Use with Unit 3, Lesson 5

Distribute a copy of the listening map to each student. Tell students that this selection is from the last symphony Beethoven wrote before he died. Unlike most symphonies, where all the music is performed by instrumentalists, the final movement of this symphony combines instruments and voices. There are four vocal soloists—a soprano, an alto, a

Listening Map Instructions

tenor, and a bass—along with a full chorus. This selection is just a part of the final movement of the symphony.

At the top of the listening map are the words "Joy. All people are brothers. When people come to the dwelling place of joy, all are united in brotherhood." These words sum up the musical theme of the movement. The top frame, which shows the orchestra's string section, represents the string fugal section of the movement. Explain to students that fugues are much like rounds. The same melody line or a variation of the melody line occurs at different times by different instruments in "layers." The melodies overlap each other.

The "Bridge/Transition" features four French horns along with the string section. There is a climactic crescendo at the end of the section.

The third section brings together the chorus along with four soloists and the orchestra. Explain to students that the words the chorus sings are in German. The lyrics were written by the famous German poet, Frederich von Schiller. The German words on the map mean:

Joy, beautiful spark of the gods, Daughter of Elysium,

We enter fire imbibed, Heavenly, thy sanctuary.

LM-10 Wade in the Water (African American spiritual)

Use with Unit 4, Lesson 5

Distribute a copy of the listening map to each student. "Wade in the Water" refers to a practice of enslaved Africans when escaping to freedom. They traveled through bodies of water to throw off the scent of bloodhounds that were tracking them. Another tactic used on the Underground Railroad was to follow the Big Dipper constellation, otherwise known as the Drinking Gourd, as a nighttime compass to the North. Ask students to name rivers that run north to south that enslaved Africans may have used to escape to freedom. The student will follow this map from the bottom left of the page, through the various verses and choruses upward toward freedom.

LM-11 Anvil Chorus from *Il Trovatore* by Giuseppe Verdi

Use with Unit 4, Lesson 6

Distribute a copy of the listening map to each student. Ask students to identify the instruments they hear. On the second listening, ask students to listen to combinations of instruments. What instrument families are combined during each section of the music?

The A and B sections see a tempo change. Ask students to create their own story of what the music is telling during these two sections. How does the anvil fit into their story?

Explain the meaning of vivace and marcato.

Listening Map Instructions

LM-13 Och Jungfrun Han Går I Ringen (Swedish dance song)

Use with Unit 5, Lesson 7

Distribute a copy of the listening map to each student. Students will listen to the recording and point to each house as the vocal part with the melody changes. Each house has four floors representing the four vocal parts. The top floor is soprano, then alto, tenor, and bass on the bottom signifying the vocal range. In each house, the singer is placed on the appropriate floor for the voice that is being heard at that time in the music. Students can follow the form of the piece by reading the labels on the roof of each house.

House:

One—sopranos

Two—baritone/tenors

Three—altos

Four—basses

Five—high tenors

Six—full choir

LM-15 Take Five by Paul Desmond

Use with Unit 6, Lesson 2

Distribute a copy of the listening map to each student. Ask students to identify the instruments they hear. Have students follow along with their finger as the music plays. In the first frame, the drum set starts the music. Have students follow the five beats on the drum-set instruments, tapping each percussion instrument once for each beat. The piano keys show the entrance of the piano. Notice that long and short images correspond to long and short notes, and the high and low pianos indicate the shape of the melody.

In frames 3–5, the melodic line is visually portrayed. Ask students to describe the tone quality and articulation of the saxophone (the sound of Paul Desmond, the saxophonist—velvety sound, precise articulation). During the saxophone solo in frame 6, have students tap their feet on beat 1 of each measure followed by clapping on beats 2 through 5. During the drum-set solo, have students do the same exercise but this time use a foot tap on beats 1 and 4.

Blue Moon of Kentucky

LISTENING MAP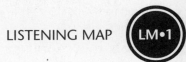

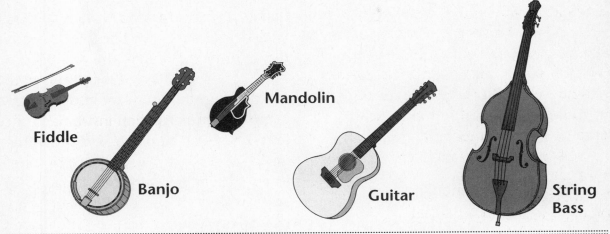

Fiddle

Mandolin

Banjo

Guitar

String Bass

$\frac{3}{4}$ Time

$\frac{2}{4}$ Time

Ode to a Butterfly

LISTENING MAP

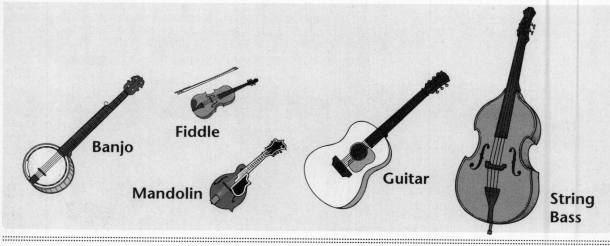

Banjo

Fiddle

Mandolin

Guitar

String Bass

Finger Picking

Melodic Picking Style

Melodic Picking Style

Using Bow

Name _____ Date _____

Maggie in the Wood
(traditional Irish song)

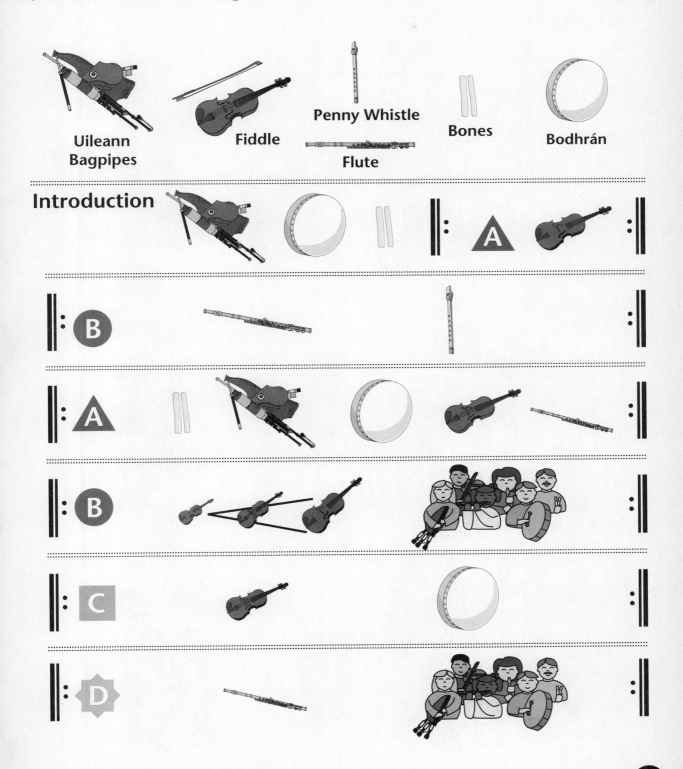

Uileann Bagpipes   Fiddle   Penny Whistle   Flute   Bones   Bodhrán

Introduction

B

A

B

C

D

Symphony No. 9 in D minor, ("Choral"), Fourth Movement
(excerpt)

LISTENING MAP

Joy. All people are brothers. When people come to the dwelling place of joy, all are united in brotherhood.

String Fugal Section

Bridge / Transition

Choral Section – Ode to Joy

Freude, schöner Götterfunken Tochter aus Elysium
Wir betreten feuertrunken Himmlische, dein Heiligtum!

Name _____ Date _____

Wade in the Water
(African American spiritual)

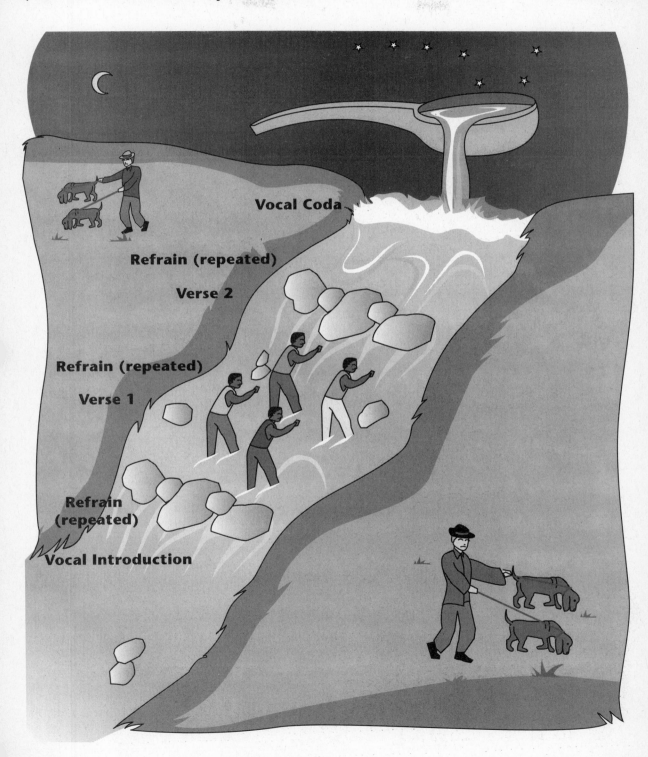

Vocal Coda

Refrain (repeated)

Verse 2

Refrain (repeated)

Verse 1

Refrain (repeated)

Vocal Introduction

Anvil Chorus from *Il Trovatore*

String Bass

Violin

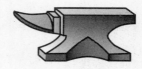
Anvil

Triangle

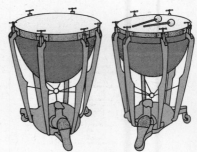
Timpani

Triangle

Piccolo

A Vivace

B Marcato

A Vivace

B Marcato

Och Jungfrun Han Går I Ringen (Swedish dance song)

LISTENING MAP

Sopranos

Tenors

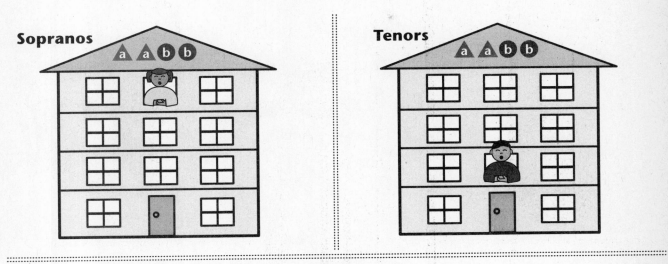

Altos

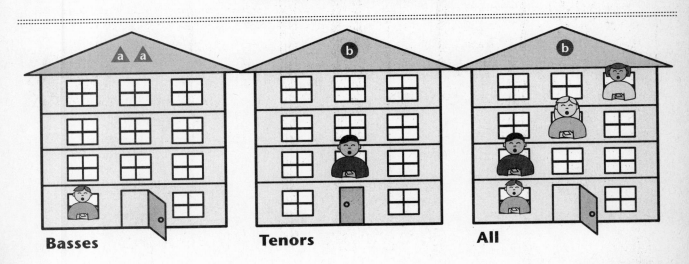

Basses   **Tenors**   **All**

Take Five

Alto Saxophone

Piano

Drum Set

String Bass

$\frac{5}{4}$ Introduction

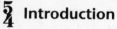

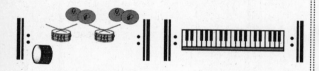

𝄋 A

B

A

Fine

Sax Solo

Drum Set Solo

D.S. al Fine

Introduction to Signed Songs

by The Reverend Dr. Peggy A. Johnson, pastor
Christ United Methodist Church of the Deaf

The use of sign language along with vocal music has become a popular way of adding interest and expression to a song. Frequently a student who struggles with vocal music will find a successful outlet for expression through the use of sign language. Sign language has been used as an educational tool for reading comprehension and language development. Typically it appears as a picture for every spoken or written English word. This is known as "Signed English." It follows the grammar of English.

American Sign Language (ASL) is different from Signed English. It uses signs for words or concepts, but the grammar is produced with the eyes and face and through the movements of the body. It does not follow the word order of spoken English for the most part and has its own structure. ASL is the native language of people who describe themselves as Culturally Deaf. Deaf Culture is a community of people consisting of deaf and hard-of-hearing people who:

• use ASL,

• have primary personal relationships with people who also use this language,

• have typically attended state residential schools for the deaf where ASL is the mode of communication and instruction, and

• have unique history, traditions, and advocacy organizations.

For people in the Deaf Culture, ASL is used in their music and poetry, not Signed English.

It is difficult for a hearing person to sing an English word-order song and to sign in ASL at the same time. Most of the sign language section of this book is done in English word-order for that reason. However, some ASL grammar is incorporated for the purpose of linguistical awareness, and ASL grammar often creates a more artistic rendering of the movements. A phrase such as "lift up your eyes" in English would be best translated into ASL as "your eyes, lift up." The latter is more effective in a signed song because ending on a sign such as "lift up" has a better flow.

Hearing people who are fascinated by and attracted to signed music might consider taking a course on ASL. It would help increase one's skill in the language. People who study "foreign" languages often develop a sensitivity for the culture and people from which the language sprang. It is a sign of respect for the culture of the people for whom this language is their native language.

A good music program provides many benefits to students and teachers. Multicultural awareness is increased when we sing songs in Spanish or German or Japanese. By "singing" in ASL, students can gain multicultural awareness of the Deaf Culture.

Rules for Signed Singing

1) Every word does not need to be signed. Keep the signs flowing one to the other, and be sensitive to the length of the word in the music. The sign for a whole-note word should be stretched out longer and slower than a quarter-note word.

2) Right-handed and left-handed people sign opposite because there is a dominant, active hand and a passive hand in many signs. For a performance, it is best to have everyone signing one way or the other, either everyone do it right-handed or everyone do it left-handed.

3) When teaching a song, it is ideal to teach it with your back to the students facing a large mirror. In that way the directionality is correct. When a teacher faces a group of students and signs, the students tend to mirror the teacher, and then the sign goes in the opposite direction.

4) A person's face needs to be appropriate to the mood of the word being sung. "Sad" should look sad, "joyful" should look joyful, etc.

5) If at all possible, invite a native signer to assist with the teaching of the song. This shows respect for the Deaf Culture, and a live example of a sign is always preferable to a drawn picture of a sign in a book.

Perfection is not the goal. The joy of music expressed in sign language can occur even when the signs are not performed perfectly.

Alphabet and Numbers

SIGNING MASTER S•1

MANUAL ALPHABET AND NUMBERS 1–10

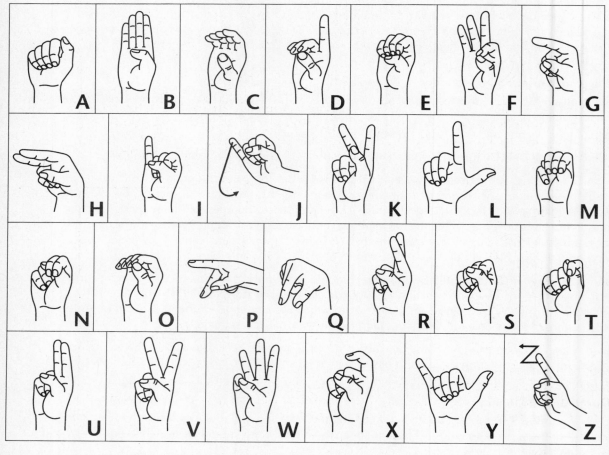

God Bless America (page 1)

1. God

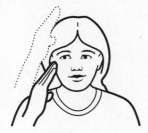

The right hand is in a letter "B" hand shape with palm facing to the left. The arm reaches up above the head and comes down to the level of the shoulder.

2. Bless

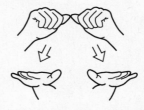

Both hands begin with a letter "A" hand shape in front of the mouth with thumbs touching and palms facing downward. Both hands slowly separate and open up into a number "5" hand shape that moves downward.

3. America

Both hands are in front of the body with fingers interlocked and fanning outward. The interlocked hands make a full circle in front of the body.

4. Land

The right hand crosses the body and makes circular motions at the elbow of the left arm.

5. Me (I)

The right index finger points to the middle of the chest.

6. Love

Hands are in a fist position and arms are crossed in front of the body like a hug.

God Bless America (page 2)

7. Allegiance (Stand beside)

Both hands are in a number "10" hand shape. The left fist is under the right fist. The left fist taps the right fist from below.

8. Her

The right index finger points to the side.

9. Through

The left hand is in a flat hand shape in front of the body, with palm facing to the right and fingertips pointing out. The right hand is in a flat hand position and it brings the hand through the left hand between the index and middle fingers.

10. Night

The left hand is positioned sideways in front of the waist with the palm downward. The right hand is placed on the left hand with the palm facing downward and the right-angle hand shape.

11. Light

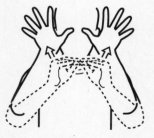

Both hands are together in a closed position in front of the body. The fingers of both hands fan outward and upward and end up on either side of the body.

12. Above

Both hands are in the right angle hand position in front of the body with palms facing downward. The left hand is above the right. The right hand makes one sweeping motion out from under the left hand and moves above the left hand.

God Bless America (page 3)

13. Mountains

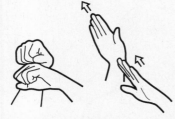

Both hands are in a letter "A" hand shape to the side of the body with the right hand on top of the left. Then both hands open to a "B" hand shape and glide upward and to the right.

14. Prairie

Both hands are in right angle hand shapes. They are in front of the body and palms are down. The right hand is in front of the left hand and they both move outward and away from the body in one continuous motion.

15. Ocean

The right hand begins the sign with a letter "W" at the lips. Then both hands make wave motions away from the body in an up and down fashion with palms facing downward.

16. My

The right hand in a "5" hand shape comes toward the body and rests on the chest.

17. Home

The right hand assumes a right angle hand shape and first touches the lips and then brings that hand across the right side of the face and lands on the check.

18. Sweet

The right hand in a flat hand shape, brushes downward in front of the mouth.

Sweet Music (page 1)

1. Music

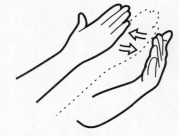

The left hand and arm are curved outward and stay stationary. The right hand, in a "B" position, swings back and forth across the left hand and arm.

2. Sweet

The right hand in a flat hand shape, brushes downward in front of the mouth.

3. Your

Right hand with palm facing away from the body pushes outward.

4. Praises

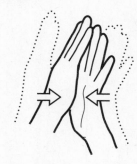

Several claps in front of the body above the shoulders.

5. We

The right index finger touches the right shoulder (pointing downward) and draws it across the body to the left shoulder.

6. Sing

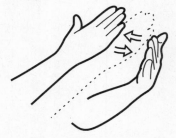

The left hand and arm are curved outward and stay stationary. The right hand, in a "B" position, swings back and forth across the left hand and arm.

Sweet Music (page 2)

SIGNING MASTER S•3

7. Tell

The index finger of the right hand starts at the mouth and goes outward.

8. Pleasure

Both hands are flat and facing the body. The right hand is higher than the left hand. Both hands make circular motions in front of the body.

9. Joy

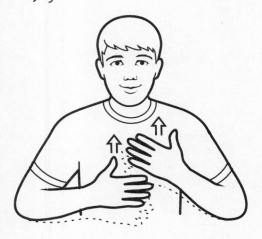

Make upward sweeps from the waist to the shoulders with both hands in a flat hand position with palms toward the body. The face should have a smiling expression.

10. Bring

Both hands are in a flat hand position in front of the body with palms facing upward. Both hands begin at the left side of the body and sweep across the body to the right side maintaining the palms-up position.

Lift Every Voice and Sing (page 1)

1. Voices

The right hand makes the "V" hand shape and brings it upward starting from the throat to the middle of the head.

2. Rise up (Lift)

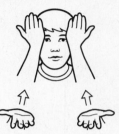

Both hands begin in a flat hand position with palms facing up in front of the body. Both hands lift upward from the waist to the head.

3. Sing

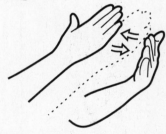

The left hand and arm are curved outward and stay stationary. The right hand, in a "B" position, swings back and forth across the left hand and arm.

4. Till

The left hand is in a number "1" hand position in front of the body with forefinger pointing upward. The right hand is also in a number "1" hand position. The right forefinger crosses over to the left forefinger and touches it.

5. Earth

The left hand is in the shape of a fist with palm facing down. The right hand thumb and forefinger grip the left hand fist and wiggle it back and forth.

6. Heaven

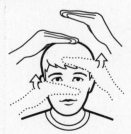

Both hands are in a slightly curved flat hand shape with palms facing downward. The hands begin to roll upward in alternate motions.

Lift Every Voice and Sing (page 2)

SIGNING MASTER S•4

7. Ring

Both hands in a number "5" hand shape on either side of the head, shaking the hands in wrist flicking motions.

8. With

Both hands are in a letter "A" hand shape in front of the body with knuckles touching.

9. Harmony

Both hands come together in front of the body in a weaving motion of the fingers. As the fingers come together the hands move downward.

10. Liberty

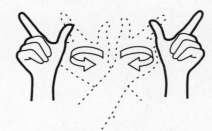

Both hands are in a letter "L" hand shape. Hands are crossed in front of the body and then breaking in opposite directions with arms extending outward.

11. Let

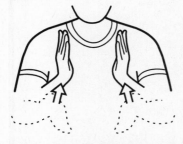

Both hands are at the sides with palms facing inward. They both point the fingertip side of the hand in an upward direction with two quick motions.

12. Joy (rejoicing)

Make upward sweeps from the waist to the shoulders with both hands in a flat hand position with palms toward the body. The face should have a smiling expression.

Lift Every Voice and Sing (page 3)

13. Rise

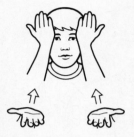

Both hands begin in a flat hand position with palms facing up in front of the body. Both hands lift upward from the waist to the head.

14. Listening

The right hand is in a number "3" hand shape. The thumb of the right hand touches the ear and the forefinger and middle finger make waving motions as if to be drawing sound into the ear.

15. Skies

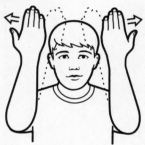

Both hands are held upward with palms facing the body. The hands are waved in opposite directions.

16. Sounds

Both hands are in a letter "S" hand shape with hands at either side of the head. The fists shake back and forth two times.

17. Same (like)

Both hands make a "Y" hand shape out in front with palms facing down. The hands move parallel across the body from left to right.

18. Ocean (Rolling Sea)

The right hand begins the sign with a letter "W" at the lips. Then both hands make wave motions away from the body in an up and down fashion with palms facing downward.

Lift Every Voice and Sing (page 4)

SIGNING MASTER **S•4**

19. Full 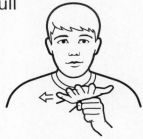 Left hand is in the letter "O" shape. It is on its side in front of the body. The right hand is in a flat hand position with the palm facing down. The right hand sweeps across the left hand from left to right.	**20. Faith**  Both hands are in a letter "F" hand shape. The right hand taps the top of the left hand.
21. Past 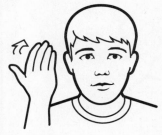 The right hand is in a flat hand position with arm upright and palm facing the body. The right hand waves over the right shoulder.	**22. Taught** 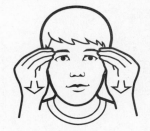 Both hands are in right angle positions at the sides of the head. Both hands make quick outward movements from the temple of the head away from the body.
23. Hope  The left arm with hand in a right angle position is held to the left side of body, slightly elevated. The right arm faces the left arm with a right angle hand position. The hands "wave" at each other.	**24. Now (Present)** 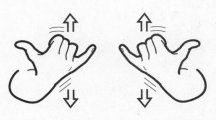 Both hands are in a letter "Y" hand shape with palms facing upward in front of the body. The hands make an up and down bouncing motion.

183

Lift Every Voice and Sing (page 5)

25. Brought

Both hands are in a flat hand position in front of the body with palms facing upward. Both hands begin at the left side of the body and sweep across the body to the right side maintaining the palms-up position.

26. Look up (facing)

Both hands are in a letter "V" hand shape with fingers pointing outward and palms facing down. Both hands slowly lift up bringing the palms and forefingers and middle fingers to an upright position.

27. Rising Sun

The left arm lays across the body with palm facing down. The right hand assumes a letter "C" hand shape. The right arm begins below the left arm and rises upward in front of the body.

28. New

The left hand is in front of the body with palm up and slightly curved. The right hand with palm up and slightly curved brushes the palm of the left hand with the back of the hand in an upward motion.

29. Day

The left arm lays across the waist with palm down. The right arm (with a hand shape of a number "1") places its elbow on the left hand. Then the right arms makes a 45 degree sweep of the arm from an upward position to its resting place on top of the left arm.

30. Begun

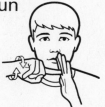

The right hand is in a number "1" hand shape. The left hand is in a number "5" hand shape with the palm facing the middle of the body. The right index finger is inserted between the index and middle finger and is twisted so that the right palm begins downward and twists upward.

Lift Every Voice and Sing (page 6)

31. March (March on)

Both hands are in a number "5" hand shape with the hands facing downward and palms toward the body. The right hand is in front of the left hand. Both hands make outward motions with the fingertips moving up and palm going from being toward to body to facing downward.

32. Victory

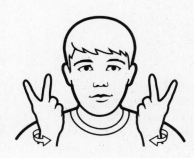

Both hands are in a "V" hand shape. Both hands are held to the side of the body and the wrists make circular motions as if waving a flag.

33. Won

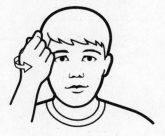

Right hand in a letter "A" hand shape. The hand is making small circular motions as if waving a flag.

What the World Needs Now (page 1)

1. What

The left hand is in a flat hand position with the palm facing the right and the fingertips pointing outward. The right hand is in a number "1" hand shape. The right hand makes one downward motion across the middle of the left palm.

2. World

Both hands form a letter "W" and then the wrists circle each other in the front of the body ending with the right wrist on top of the left wrist.

3. Needs

The right hand is in a letter "X" hand shape with the palm facing downward in front of the body. The hand nods up and down.

4. Now

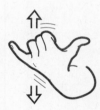

Both hands are in a letter "Y" hand shape with palms facing upward in front of the body. The hands make an up and down bouncing motion.

5. Love

Hands are in a fist position and arms are crossed in front of the body like a hug.

6. Sweet

The right hand in a flat hand shape, brushes downward in front of the mouth.

What the World Needs Now (page 2)

7. Truly (it's)

The index finger of the right hand begins at the mouth and extends outward.

8. Only

The right hand is in a number "1" hand shape with arm pointing upward and palm facing inward. The index finger makes one small circle as it points upward.

9. Thing

The right hand is in a slightly cupped flat hand position with palm facing upward to the right of the body. The hand makes two bouncing movements to the right.

10. Not

Both hands are crossed in front of the body with palms facing downward. Then the hands cross in front of the body and arms end up extended on both sides.

11. Enough

The left hand is in a letter "O" hand shape on its side with the palm facing the right. The right hand is in a flat hand position with palm facing down. The right hand makes two quick sweeps across the top of the left hand away from the body.

12. Only (just)

The right hand is in a number "1" hand shape with arm pointing upward and palm facing inward. The index finger makes one small circle as it points upward.

What the World Needs Now (page 3)

13. For

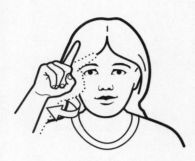

The right index finger touches the forehead and then the finger is moved away from the head dipping the finger down and then back up.

14. Some

The left hand is in a flat hand position in front of the body with palm upward. The right hand is in a flat hand position with the palm facing left. The right hand makes a cutting motion across the left palm, pulling the hand toward the body.

15. But

Both hands assume a number "1" hand shape in front of the body with index fingers crossed. Then the fingers separate to opposite sides.

16. Everyone

Both hands are in a number "10" hand shape in front of the body. The right hand brushes along side the left hand two times and then ends with the right hand forming a number "1" hand shape pointing upward.

Name _____ Date _____

We Want to Sing (page 1)

1. We

The right index finger touches the right shoulder (pointing downward) and draws it across the body to the left shoulder.

2. Want

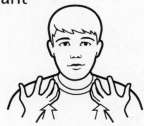

Both hands are in a claw position with palms up and extended away from the body. Both hands draw the claw toward the body and curl the fingers a little inward as it moves closer to the body.

3. Sing

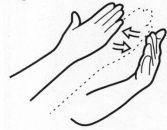

The left hand and arm are curved outward and stay stationary. The right hand, in a "B" position, swings back and forth across the left hand and arm.

4. Tell

The index finger of the right hand starts at the mouth and goes outward.

5. World

Both hands form a letter "W" and then the wrists circle each other in the front of the body ending with the right wrist on top of the left wrist.

6. Inform (them to know)

Both hands are in a closed position at the top of the head. The hands are brought down and the palms open up in front of the body.

We Want to Sing (page 2)

7. Love

Hands are in a fist position and arms are crossed in front of the body like a hug.

8. With

Both hands are in a letter "A" hand shape in front of the body with knuckles touching.

9. Our

The right hand begins with a right angle hand shape at the right shoulder. The hand then sweeps across the body and ends at the left shoulder.

10. Music

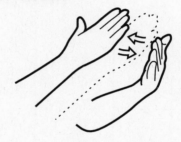

The left hand and arm are curved outward and stay stationary. The right hand, in a "B" position, swings back and forth across the left hand and arm.

11. Can

Both hands are in a letter "A" hand shape in front of the body with palms facing downward. The hands make a quick up and down motion.

12. Make

Both hands are in the shape of a fist. The right hand taps the the left hand Then both wrists twist in place and the right and left hands tap again.

We Want to Sing (page 3)

13. Better

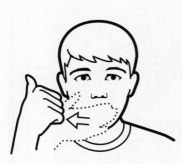

The right hand is in a flat hand position with the palm toward the body. The right hand sweeps across the mouth and the fingers close into a letter "A" hand shape as it passes the head.

14. Place

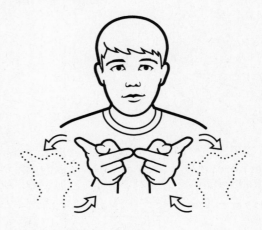

Both hands are in a letter "P" hand shape facing each other with the middle fingers touching out in front of the body. Both hands make semi circle out and then inward with the middle fingers touching once again close to the body.

15. For

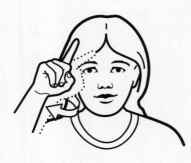

The right index finger touches the forehead and then the finger is moved away from the head dipping the finger down and then back up.

16. Everyone

Both hands are in a number "10" hand shape in front of the body. The right hand brushes along side the left hand two times and then ends with the right hand forming a number "1" hand shape pointing upward.

I Got Rhythm (page 1)

SIGNING MASTER S•7

1. Me (I)  The right index finger points to the middle of the chest.	**2. Have (got)**  Both hands touch the chest with a right angle hand shape.
3. Rhythm  The left hand is in a letter "A" hand shape in front of the body with the palm facing down. The right hand is in a letter "R" position. The right hand taps the back of the left hand two times.	**4. Music** 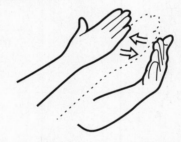 The left hand and arm are curved outward and stay stationary. The right hand, in a "B" position, swings back and forth across the left hand and arm.
5. My  The right hand in a "5" hand shape comes toward the body and rests on the chest.	**6. Friends** Both hands in an "X" shape with forefingers linking once with the right hand on top and then a second linking motion with the left hand on top.

I Got Rhythm (page 2)

SIGNING MASTER S•7

7. Who

The right hand is in a number "1" hand shape and it makes a counter clockwise circle around the mouth.

8. Can (Could)

Both hands are in a letter "A" hand shape in front of the body with palms facing downward. The hands make a quick up and down motion.

9. Ask

Both hands are joined in a flat hand position in front of the body with palms touching.

10. For

The right index finger touches the forehead and then the finger is moved away from the head dipping the finger down and then back up.

11. Anything

The right hand is in a letter "A" hand shape. It begins with the palm toward the body, swings it out away from the body and then the hand shape changes to a flat hand shape with palm up. The flat hand shape makes two motions toward the right.

12. More

Both hands are in a right angle hand shape with the fingers touch in front of the body. The fingers tap together two times.

I Got Rhythm (page 3)

SIGNING MASTER S•7

13. Flower

The right hand is in a right angle shape with the fingers closed. It touches the right side of the nose and then crosses over to the left side of the nose.

14. Pastures

Both hands are in a number "5" hand shape in front of the body with palms facing down. The hands go in opposite directions in a circular motion and then back to the front of the body but slightly extended.

15. Old

The right hand reaches up to the chin in a squeezing motion and then the right hand pulls downward with a letter "S" hand shape.

16. Man

The right hand makes a right angle hand shape at the forehead. Then the right hand moves away from the head toward the center of the chest and assume a number "5" hand shape.

17. Trouble

Both hands are in a letter "B" hand shape with arms lifted up and palms facing each other. The hands make circles around the face going in a clock wise direction.

18. Don't

Both hands are crossed in front of the body with palms facing downward. Then the hands cross in front of the body and arms end up extended on both sides.

I Got Rhythm (page 4)

SIGNING MASTER   S•7

---

19. Pay Attention (mind him)

Both hands are in a flat hand position with palms facing each other on either side of the head. Both hands make two quick forward motions.

20. You

Index finger on the right hand points outward.

---

21. Won't

The right hand is in a letter "A" hand shape. The arm is in an upright position and the palm faces toward the left. The right hand makes one quick backward motion resembling a hitch hiking movement.

22. Find

The right hand is in a letter "F" hand shape. It reaches out and appears to pick up something in front of it with the index finger and thumb and then draws it up toward the body.

---

23. Him

The right index finger points to the side.

24. Near (round)

The left and right hands are in a curved hand shape in front of the body with palms facing the body. The left hand is farther from the body. The right hand makes a movement toward the left hand.

195

I Got Rhythm (page 5)

25. Door

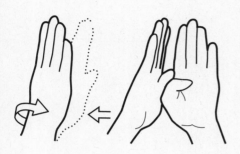

Both hands are in a letter "B" hand shape with thumbs touching, and hands pointing upward with palms facing outward. The right hand pulls away from the left hand and the wrist turns making the palm turn inward.

26. Stars

Both hands are lifted above the head with index fingers extended and pointing upwards. The fingers rub against each other in an up and down motion.

27. Dreams

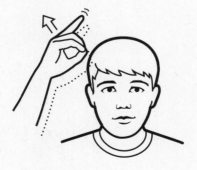

The right hand is in a letter "D" hand shape. The right hand pulls the letter "D" from the top of the head upward and wiggles the index finger as it pulls upward.

Grade 5 Answer Key

1•4 Rhythm 4 You

1. The sixth beat in line b should be circled.

2. The third, fourth, seventh, and eighth beats in line b should be circled.

3. The first through fourth beats and the sixth and seventh beats in line b should be circled.

4. a   5. a

6.–10. Students can fill in any of the three selections in each blank to make four-beat rhythms.

1•5 C-Pentatonic Scale

1. b   6. E G C A
2. d   7. A D G E
3. e   8. G A E C
4. a   9. A G G E
5. c   10. D A D G

1•6 Caribbean Cruise

Cuba: son

Jamaica: reggae

Puerto Rico: bomba

Dominican Republic: merengue

1•7 Song Ranges

1. C   2. D

3. The range is nine notes, or an octave plus one note.

4. B   5. D

6. The range is ten notes, or an octave plus two notes.

1•8 Mid-Unit Review

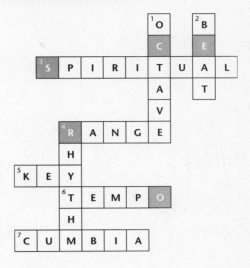

Bonus Word: score (written music that has all the parts arranged one on top of the other)

1•11 Musical Form

The form for "Little David Play on Your Harp" is A B A.

1•12 Name That Symbol!

1. e   6. o   11. a
2. g   7. b   12. n
3. h   8. i   13. k
4. m   9. l   14. f
5. d   10. c   15. j

2•5 Korean Percussion Instruments

1. janggu   7. kkwaenaggwari
2. jing   8. jing
3. janggu   9. janggu
4. buk   10. janggu
5. buk   11. kkwaenaggwari
6. jing   12. kkwaenaggwari

Grade 5 Answer Key

2•6 Don't Wait—Syncopate!

1. Students should cross out "I want pi-zza and cake." and "Al-li-ga-tors can bite." Their own rhythm patterns will vary. You can check the accuracy as you listen to them play.

2. Students' rhythms will vary. You can check the accuracy as you hear them play.

2•7 Playing with Pentatonics

1. and 2.

2•8 Mid-Unit Review

3. The Fung *Yang* Song is a *flower* drum song. This traditional *Chinese* song comes from street performers. This *folk* song is very old. Often, dancers perform this song wearing a *dragon* costume.

a.–b.

Melody b is melody a, transposed from the key of D to C. All of the letters from melody a are 1 letter lower in melody b.

2•8 Mid-Unit Review

1. j	6. l	11. g
2. e	7. b	12. m
3. i	8. a	13. f
4. d	9. k	
5. c	10. h	

2•10 Reviewing and Composing Rhythms

1. $\frac{2}{4}$	5. $\frac{4}{4}$
2. $\frac{2}{4}$	6. $\frac{2}{4}$
3. $\frac{3}{4}$	7. $\frac{3}{4}$
4. $\frac{4}{4}$	8. $\frac{3}{4}$

Grade 5 Answer Key

2•11 The Percussion of Ghana

Gankonqui
- has a higher and a lower-pitched bell
- double bell held in the hand and struck with a stick

Atoke
- used to play the beat
- held flat in the palm and hit with a stick

Axatse
- made from a dried gourd surrounded with strings of beads
- shaker

Kidi
- sounds like the sogo, but higher

Sogo
- makes a low booming sound
- larger version of the Kidi, played with sticks while sitting

3•4 Clapping and Tapping in $^6_8$

Students' lyrics and rhythms will vary. Check to see that their rhythm ostinatos work well with "De colores."

3•5 A Closer Look at "Mango Walk"

3•7 Composing Music for a Poem

Check students' compositions for the accuracy of the meter and the harmony of the thirds.

3•8 Mid-Unit Review

¹A	C	C	I	D	E	N	T	²A	L	S			³W	
								R					H	
			⁴C	O	U	N	T	E	R	M	E	L	O	O	Y
			O					A					L	
			⁵M	A	J	O	R	N		⁶M	E	T	E	R
			P					G						
			⁷G	O	S	P	E	L		E				
			U					M						
			N				⁸I	N	T	E	R	V	A	L
			D					N						
					⁹D	I	A	T	O	N	I	C		

Grade 5 Answer Key

3•12 Sorting Out Musical Terminology!

1. Possible answers:
   Tempo: speed of the music
   Dynamics: variations in volume, intensity, or mood of music
   Articulation: manner of expressing individual notes, such as playing a note longer, shorter, or with extra emphasis
   Tone color: determined by specific instruments or voices used in music

2. Possible answers:

Tempo	Dynamics	Articulation
accelerando	crescendo	staccato
ritardando	decrescendo	legato
fermata		accent

3. Possible answers:
   accelerando is the opposite of *ritardando*
   ritardando is the opposite of *a tempo*
   legato is the opposite of *staccato*

4•4 Counting Sixteenths

Students' answers will vary. For number 2, make sure that each measure has two full beats.

4•5 Major and Minor

1.

   do re mi fa so la ti do

2. A minor

4•6 Practice Major and Minor

1. G major, E minor

2.

Major		Minor
C Major		A Minor
G Major		E Minor

Major		Minor
F Major		D Minor
D Major		B Minor

3.

   B minor

4•9 Mid-Unit Review

1. Answers will vary. Check to see that students have followed the guidelines.

2. D major

3.

   B minor

4. The two notes were connected together with a *slur.*
   I played all four notes together in a *chord.*
   She loves to *improvise* when she sings.
   He added a third note to make a *triad.*
   The *root* of the triad was middle C.

Grade 5 Answer Key

4•10 Reviewing Meter Signatures

Staff 1. $\frac{3}{4}$ Staff 5. $\frac{6}{8}$

Staff 2. $\frac{4}{4}$ Staff 6. $\frac{2}{2}$

Staff 3. $\frac{6}{8}$ Staff 7. $\frac{4}{4}$

Staff 4. $\frac{2}{4}$

5•4 The Main Chord

1. C   2. F   3. G

4.

5•6 The Blues of "Backwater Blues"

5•7 Singin' the Blues

Students' lyrics will vary. Check to see that they match the rhythm and rhyme.

5•8 Mid-Unit Review

1. c   3. h   5. b   7. d

2. a   4. e   6. f   8. g

6•4 Identifying Meter Signatures

1. "Somewhere Over the Rainbow," $\frac{4}{4}$

2. "America," $\frac{3}{4}$

3. "Turn the World Around," $\frac{5}{8}$

4. "Row, Row, Row Your Boat," $\frac{2}{4}$

5. "Follow the Yellow Brick Road," $\frac{6}{8}$

6•5 Downbeats and Upbeats

Numbers 1, 3, and 5 begin on upbeats.

Numbers 2, 4, and 6 begin on downbeats.

6•7 Mid-Unit Review

1. k   5. l   9. g

2. e   6. m   10. h

3. i   7. d

4. f   8. c

Grade 5 Answer Key

6•8 Map of Native American Nations

1. Seminole or Creek (red color)
2. Navajo (yellow color)
3. students' state (green color)
4. New York

6•11 Labeling Percussion Instruments

1. timpani
2. triangle
3. maracas
4. snare drum
5. bass drum
6. xylophone
7. gong
8. castanets
9. cymbals
10. tom-tom
11. tambourine
12. woodblock

C•1 Chusok

Special Food: song pyon

Special Smell: pine

Special Activity: visiting and caring for ancestors' graves

C•3 Halloween Puzzle

								¹C	
		²S						A	
³J	A	C	K	O	⁴L	A	N	⁵T	E	R	N
A		E		A		R		D	
⁶Z	E	A	L			⁷E	A	S	Y
Z		E	M		⁸M	A			
		T		⁹W	I	T	C	¹⁰H	
¹¹B	O	O		N			A	
		N		¹²C	O	S	T	U	M	E
				R			N	
				K			T	
				E			E	
	¹³G	R	A	V	E	Y	A	R	D

C•5 Winter Word Scramble

1. SNOWBOARD
2. HOCKEY
3. SKATES
4. WONDERLAND
5. ICICLE
6. TOBOGGAN
7. JACKET
8. SNOWSHOES
9. MITTENS
10. BLIZZARD

C•8 Cinco de Mayo

The country fighting against Mexico: France

The Mexican town where the battle took place: Puebla

The date of the battle: May 5, 1862

C•9 Powwow Dances

1. e
2. a
3. b
4. d
5. c
6. h
7. f
8. g